Trees and Trails

New York 1952

Trees and Trails

BY CLARENCE J. HYLANDER

THE MACMILLAN COMPANY

First Printing

Printed in the United States of America

TO MY MOTHER

whose love of fragrant woods
of pine and fir
is equalled only by
her zest for life

CONTENTS

An hour, a day, or a month spent in exploring forest trails can become the memorable moment of our lives if we know trees both as individuals and as members of a forest community.

Chapter 1

THE LIFE OF A TREE

FEW LIVING THINGS have been as useful to man as trees, or as constantly sought for companionship. The bare earth around our houses becomes the setting for a home when trees are planted to contribute their leafy personality. Towns, states, and our national government have spent large sums to preserve American forests and to stimulate the care of trees.

Trees command our interest and respect for their many special abilities, among them their tremendous growth and long life. They are the only living things which have been able to stretch the life span into thousands of years. They are also the only forms of life which attain a stature of three hundred feet and more. Trees are constructive members of the living community, quietly making life more pleasant for all of us.

From our childhood, with its numerous outdoor activities, to our adult existence of work, play and travel, trees are always around us and a part of our experiences. The trees we remember may have been spruces marching in dark green ranks to the edge of the ocean, spruces in whose branches hid scolding chipmunks and pert chickadees. They may have been the hickories and butternuts of a Connecticut field whose leafless branches swayed in the autumn sunshine as we scuffed through the fallen leaves in search of nuts. They may have been redbuds on a North Carolina hillside or dogwoods of an Indiana woodland, clothed in rose-colored and white blossoms, or swamp maple and sweet gum bringing vivid reds to the autumn colors of a Maryland or Virginia lowland.

If our home was in the South, the trees of our childhood were, perhaps, the cypresses in a Louisiana bayou where we ventured cautiously in search of turtles or catfish. Or the trees may have been slash pine and cabbage palm in a Florida flatwoods, through which we wandered in search of 'coon and rabbit.

If we lived in the western states, our tree neighbors may have been the silvery blue spruces on the slopes of the Colorado mountains, or the groves of aspen poplar in the Arizona foothills. They may have been live oaks on a brown California hillside, offering grateful shade from the summer's sun, or fragrant eucalyptus trees lining the streets along which we passed on our way to school. They may even have been the towering redwoods of the Pacific Coast, through whose shadowy aisles deer moved silently over the thick brown carpet of needles.

Whatever the particular trees we remember, they were our friends, clothed every month of the year with a different beauty, inviting in their shade, fascinating in the variety of their foliage, flower, and fruit.

If city dwellers, we perhaps found that trees meant more to us than to those who lived with a great forest at their door. We may remember the hardy ailanthus which brought a welcome touch of nature to barren city streets. We certainly remember such magnificent visitors from the country as the spruces and firs, erected every Christmas, indoors and out, and decked in festive attire for the holiday season.

What Is a Tree?

A tree is a woody plant which lives from year to year; that is, it is a perennial. It is capable of growing to considerable size when given favorable living conditions, differing from a shrub in having only one or a few main stems. A tree is the most complex type of plant, its position among other plants corresponding to that held by a mammal in the animal kingdom. Every tree is constructed according to a basically similar blueprint, whose specifications are followed, with only minor variations, in all kinds of trees. This pattern includes six organs, each carrying on a special activity which benefits the tree as a whole.

Three of these organs cooperate in keeping the individual tree alive. Known as vegetative organs, they are the roots, the stems (trunk) and the leaves. *Roots* are underground structures which absorb water and minerals from the soil and act as anchors to keep the tree firmly in place. The *stem,* which forms the main axis of the tree, is commonly called the trunk; this is actually a direct continuation of the main root. Smaller stems are formed by branching, producing the intricate framework which acts as the skeleton of the tree, supporting tons of foliage and fruit. *Leaves,* the most numerous of all the organs, manufacture the food essential for the tree's life. In some kinds of trees (the evergreens) all three vegetative organs are present at all times of the year; others (the deciduous trees) are leafless in winter and thus at that time of year consist only of roots and stems. The stems, however, bear buds within which is the undeveloped foliage of the next growing season.

The other three organs are those which cooperate to produce new trees. Known as reproductive organs, they are present only when the tree is mature, sometimes ten or twelve years after the tree begins its life. Even then, reproductive organs are present only for a brief period every year. These are the seeds, fruits, and either cones or flowers.

The *seed* is an organ found normally in all trees; in other words, all trees are seed-producing plants. Within each seed is the immature miniature plant, or embryo. The seed also contains enough stored food to keep the baby tree alive until germination is completed. In this way the seed of a tree is very much like the egg of a bird, which contains both the bird embryo and a generous supply of food.

Seeds are formed as the result of the activity of pollen and egg producing structures which vary considerably in appearance. The most familiar is the *flower,* with typically bright colors and fragrance. Some tree flowers are conspicuous, as is true of the cherries, magnolias, catalpa, and horse chestnut. Others are less easy to see, such as the flowers of maples and elms. Still other trees—notably the willows and poplars—have small flowers clustered in tassels known as catkins.

Many familiar trees, of which the pines and spruces are examples, do not produce flowers of any type but instead develop pollen and egg structures in *cones.* For this reason the trees of this group are known as conifers, or cone-bearers.

A third type of reproductive structure is the *fruit*. This is a ripened portion of the flower, surrounding the seeds. Fruits are therefore found only in flowering trees. Familiar tree fruits are the winged "keys" of the maples, the berries of a dogwood, the pods of locusts, and the acorns of oaks.

A Tree Begins Its Life

With the approach of late summer and autumn we witness the annual scattering of the fruits and seeds, some being carried by the wind, others on the fur of animals or attached to clothing, still others being transported by animals prizing the fruits as food. Even those which are eaten usually survive their experience in the animal's stomach, protected by the seed coat, and emerge to germinate as nature intended.

Most tree seeds are so small that it is difficult to see the embryo without the aid of a magnifying lens, thus we can best discover what a plant looks like at this early stage in its life by examining the contents of a bean seed. When the seed coats are removed, the embryo is seen to consist of two tightly-fitting halves known as seed-leaves or cotyledons. Lying between the plump cotyledons and attached to them is the remainder of the embryo; it consists of a slim curved tip at one end and some small folded leaves at the other. These are important parts of the baby plant. The pointed tip is the beginning of a root, the folded leaves are the first bud, and the short section between is the embryonic stem. Thus even at this early age the infant tree consists of all three vegetative organs: root, stem, and leaves.

The cotyledons are important accessories in that they contain the stored food upon which the seedling depends during the early stages of its germination.

Some tree seeds, for example those of the maples, germinate the same year they are produced. Many seeds however lie inactive during the winter or dry season, unharmed by low temperatures or drought. It has been proved that many seeds can remain alive for a hundred years or more and still be capable of germination. When the warm days of spring or the wet days of the rainy season arrive, the seeds "come to life." Germination means a renewal of the growth process which was temporarily halted when the fruit became mature. In order to germinate, as any gardener knows from experience, the seed requires warmth and moisture; light and soil are not necessary.

As the seed coats soften and break open, the root emerges. With a special ability to recognize "up" from "down," the tip of the root pushes its way into the earth, no matter how the seed happens to lie. Soon a tiny but effective root system is anchoring the seedling in place, at the same time absorbing water and minerals from the soil. Soon too the shoot is unfolding and pushing its way through the seed coat. It also can sense "up" from "down" and reacts to gravity, but in an opposite fashion. Instead of growing downward the shoot rises upward, bringing the foliage-bearing stem to the light. The cotyledons, having served their purpose, wither and disappear as the bud of the seedling produces sufficient leaves to keep the young tree alive.

Foliage Keeps the Tree Alive

All trees are green plants. The green color is caused by the presence of *chlorophyll,* a unique compound found almost without exception only in plants. When a part of the living substance, or protoplasm, of the plant cell, chlorophyll brings about the most vital chemical reaction known to man. Using sunlight as a source of energy, the chlorophyll-protoplasm mechanism transforms ordinary air and water into food. This food is sugar, which may be used directly by the tree as a source of energy for growth and other activities, or it may be transformed into cellulose, starch, oil, or protein for other uses within the tree. The name of this important food-manufacturing process is *photosynthesis.* With it, plants can make their own food; without it, organisms such as animals have to eat their food.

In most trees the green color is concentrated in the leaves. The few exceptions are the tree cacti, the outer bark of young twigs (readily seen in sassafras), the outer parts of flowers, and the outer layers of unripe fruits. Foliage is so typical of trees that it is difficult for many persons to recognize different kinds of trees when they are leafless. They may even consider a tree dead when it lacks leaves. Peculiarities in the distribution of trees, the age of trees, their evergreen or deciduous habit, the appearance and size of leaves in different kinds of trees, can often be explained by understanding the work that leaves do.

The broad thin leaf of a maple or oak is typical of the deciduous trees which lose their leaves in winter or during the dry season. The leaf surface is protected by a layer of cells with a tough outer covering and perforated by millions of minute pores which permit air to pass in and out of the leaf. This is essential because air contains the carbon dioxide used in photosynthesis. The disadvantage of a perforated surface however is that it allows moisture to evaporate from the interior of the leaf, thus reducing the water supply available for food manufacture. Especially is this true in winter when the soil water freezes; at this time trees with thin broad leaves need to conserve water. The deciduous trees adapt themselves to this situation by being leafless until warm weather of spring returns. When the leaves are shed, photosynthesis ceases; as a result the tree goes into a resting stage until a new set of leaves is produced.

Some of the broad-leaved trees, such as holly and live oaks, are evergreen. These grow in mild climates. Most of the evergreen trees in cold climates are the conifers, which are suited to retain their foliage the year round. Their small needle-like leaves have fewer pores, and are protected by a thick glossy covering. Such needle-like leaves are not as efficient in summer as the deciduous type. But because the needle-type is more capable of doing some photosynthetic work every month of the year, the northern and high-altitude forests are made up mainly of spruces, pines, firs and other conifers.

Within the protective layer, leaves have one or several layers of cells where the chlorophyll is concentrated. This is the green tissue of the leaf and the actual food-manufacturing center. In most leaves the green tissue is just below the upper surface where it can intercept the maximum amount of sunlight. Below this is a more spongy tissue, filled with air spaces and conducting tubes which can be likened to the passageways and freight elevators in a factory. The air spaces conduct the air from the pores to the green tissue. The tubes, which form the "veins" of the leaves, transport water to the same green tissue as well as the manufactured sugar away from it. The veins lead into the larger ones which form the midrib of the leaf; it in turn connects with the larger conducting tubes in the stem, trunk, and roots.

Securing adequate supplies of air is not difficult. Water, however, often presents a greater problem. With diminished rainfall the food-manufacturing process has to slow down for want of one of the raw materials. As the food supply of the tree decreases, growth becomes retarded and the tree as a whole becomes stunted. Unless a tree has

How a Tree Makes Its Food.

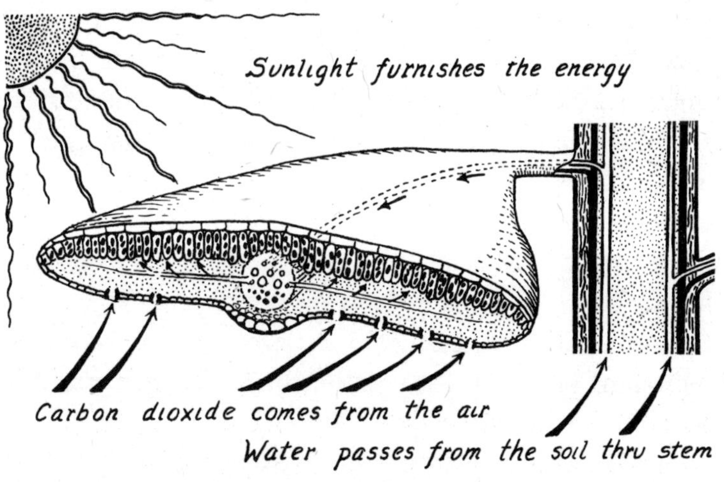

Food is made in the leaf cells by the chloroplasts

healthy leaves it cannot grow as it should and live to its maximum age. Likewise, a prolonged drought can kill all the leaves of a tree; if the leafless condition occurs at a critical period in the tree's growth, death usually is the result.

The importance of sunlight is evident when we realize that without a source of energy the food-manufacturing machinery must come to a standstill, as does a car without gasoline. Many tree seedlings die because they happen to germinate in the dim light under a dense screen of foliage on older trees. Most trees engage in a never-ending competition to get to the light, the race being won by the tree which can raise its foliage higher and spread it wider than its neighbors. Along many a forest trail you can see long slender tree trunks growing at an awkward angle, aiming at an opening in the forest canopy where a bit of sky promises working space for the chlorophyll.

The temperature of the air is important because low temperatures retard chemical reactions and high temperatures tend to speed them up. In the northern states, when autumn weather brings with it near-freezing temperatures, the photosynthetic process ceases because the chlorophyll-protoplasm combination disintegrates. As the green color disappears other pigments already present in the leaf become exposed, resulting in the display of orange and yellow colors. At the same time, in some trees, sugars are transformed into red pigments. After a week or two, with food manufacture at a standstill, the leaf dies, turning a lifeless brown in the process. Finally the weakened leaf stalk breaks at its junction with the stem and the leaf falls to the ground; its life was a short but an active one.

The Trunk Produces Wood

Trunks and branches are very different from leaves in their growth habits. Leaves have a definite limit to their size, growth terminating when the leaf reaches its predetermined dimensions. Maple leaves vary considerably in size, but no maple leaf normally is as large as that of a catalpa; and a catalpa rarely attains the size of a palm leaf. Stems however have an ability to grow indefinitely. This means that the trunk, branches, and smaller stems can grow continually both in diameter and in length. The height and bulk of the tree are determined chiefly by the structural features which give the trunk the ability to resist the stresses of wind storms, ice, and snow and to support the weight of its foliage. This ability varies sufficiently among different kinds of trees so that the maximum height of various species is often a characteristic of the tree. Some are relatively small, such as the dogwood and gray birch; others are medium sized trees, such as maples and oaks; a few reach unusual stature as can be seen among the species of Sequoia, spruces and firs.

The one-year-old seedling has a "trunk" made up of spongy tissues through which a few conducting tubes form channels extending from the roots to the leaves. These take care of the upward flow of water to the green tissues of the leaves, and the downward flow of sugar solution (sap) from the leaves to regions of storage. So few leaves are produced the first year that the frail axis can support them, even though it has little strengthening material to act as a skeleton.

In succeeding years more and more foliage is produced,

and at the same time the stem increases a little in diameter each year. This is caused by the activity of a special growth tissue, or cambium, which is capable of producing new conducting tubes and, mixed with them, special supporting cells. The walls of the tubes are themselves able to lend some support to the stem because of the occurrence of cellulose. These cellulose-walled tubes and the special supporting cells form the *wood*. The cambium tissue, outside the woody tissue, forms a hollow cylinder just beneath the surface of the stem. Each year the cambium cylinder moves outward a little, producing new woody tissues inside of it. As the growth of the trunk continues, more and more of its bulk is wood, which acts as a supporting skeleton for an increasingly greater weight of branches and foliage.

A familiar feature of wood is the series of rings which begin as small circles in the middle of the stem, and become larger and larger toward the region of the bark. These are the growth rings, sometimes inaccurately

How a Tree Makes Wood.

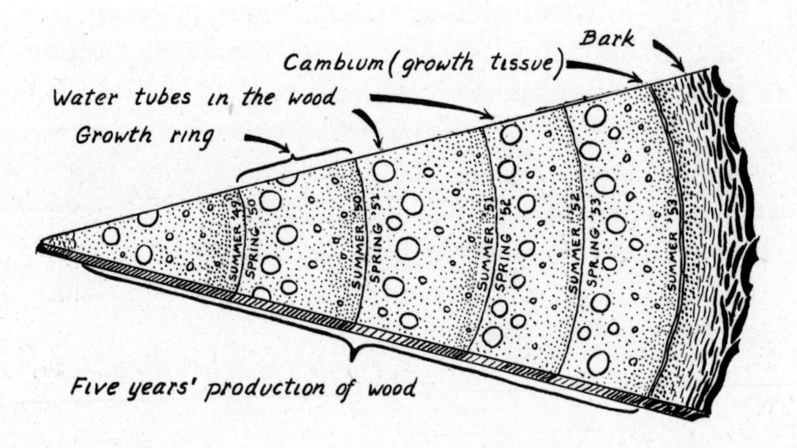

termed annual rings. When the growth activity of the cambium ceases, the conducting tubes most recently formed are of smaller diameter and thicker walls. When growth is resumed, the first tubes formed are of greater diameter and have thin walls. This results in a rather clear-cut boundary between the last-formed summer wood and the newly-formed spring wood. Each growth ring therefore begins at its inner portion with thin-walled tubes formed in early spring and summer, and ends with the thick-walled tubes formed in late summer. By counting the number of rings in a woody stem one can estimate the number of growing seasons. In the northern states, where trees have one growth period and one rest period a year, the ring is an "annual" ring and can give the approximate age of the tree in years. But in regions of several alternating growth and rest periods a year, there may be several growth rings annually. The size of the growth rings, the nature of their conducting cells, and other features associated with ring formation are important in determining the grain of wood, its hardness or softness, and its suitability for various lumber uses.

The trunk of a seedling has on the outside the same type of protective tissue found on the outer surface of leaves; thus these immature trunks bruise easily. After a few years a more durable protective tissue develops, becoming bark. Since the trunk is constantly increasing in diameter the bark has to split open to accommodate the expanding girth. As a result the bark of most trees is furrowed, shredded, or peels off in layers. You have undoubtedly noticed this in the shagbark hickory, the birches, and eucalyptus.

The Seed Completes the Life Cycle

The combined efforts of roots, stems, and leaves have now brought the tree to maturity. At this time the reproductive activities can begin. Special buds develop at the tips of the stems, or sometimes at the junction of the stems. Inside these buds are produced the reproductive organs. A flowering tree, such as an apple, can serve as an example of the sequence of events.

As the flower bud opens, the various parts unfold in definite order. The outermost green segments form the sepals. They completely protected the flower when it was a bud and remain to support the colored petals which form a second series of flower parts. Both sepals and petals occur in the apple blossom. Many tree flowers lack one or both of these flower parts.

When the blossom is fully formed, at its center can be seen the actual reproductive structures: the stamens, whose tips will produce the golden-yellow pollen dust, and the central greenish pistil. Hidden from view in the bottom of the pistil are one or more plant eggs. An important step in the reproductive process is the means by which the tiny pollen grains are brought to the tip of the pistil. Birds, insects, and winds bring this about. Once a pollen grain lodges on the pistil it grows into the tissues of the pistil and unites with an egg. Every egg which is thus joined by a pollen grain becomes an embryo with all of the parts we have already described.

These reproductive events are invisible but their progress is signalled by the loss of petals, the withering of the stamens, and often the decrease in size or loss of the sepals.

How Trees Produce Seeds.

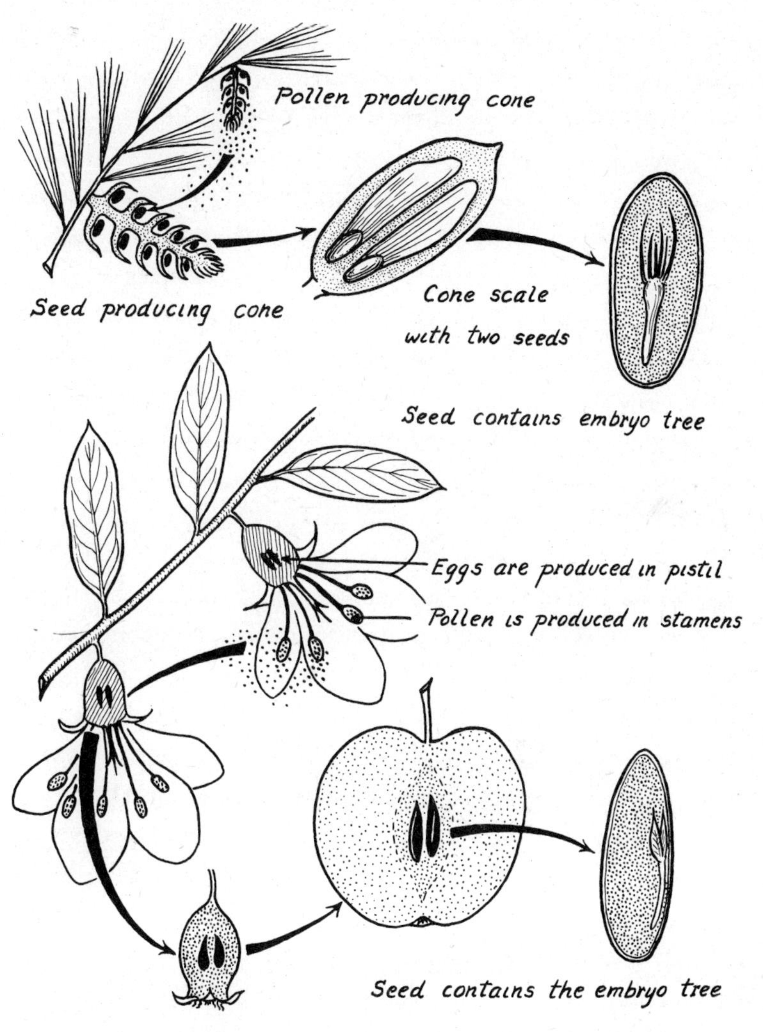

A most obvious change is the swelling of the base of the pistil; this grows larger and larger, soon assuming the shape of a small apple. Thus the lower portion of the pistil becomes the fruit, within which are the seeds, and within each seed is the minute embryo of a new apple tree.

In trees which produce cones instead of flowers the reproductive process begins with the formation of two kinds of cones. Many small cones are produced within which pollen grains develop. The egg-producing structures are large cones, comparatively few in number. As the small cones open, the pollen is scattered by the wind as a fine golden dust, some of which settles by chance on an egg-producing cone, whose scales have separated enough to allow the pollen to enter. From this point on the process is much the same as in the apple tree. However, after the seed is formed it is left unprotected on the surface of the cone scale. When the cone scales open farther, the seeds fall out, often being aided in their voyaging by the wind. There is no fruit. The old open cones become woody and may remain for several years on the tree as evidence of the completion of a life cycle. New cones, like new flowers, are formed every year the reproductive process is repeated.

This has been but a glimpse of the events that take place in the life of a tree. It has, perhaps, given you a picture of the tree as a living organism and explained some of the major changes which take place in stems, leaves, flowers and seeds. It will be helpful in understanding many of the features which are important in learning to identify trees.

Chapter 2

HOW TREES DIFFER FROM EACH OTHER

AT FIRST SIGHT one might think that all trees are alike, since they have roots, trunks, leaves, produce wood and provide for offspring by reproductive structures often very similar in appearance. There are some seven hundred different kinds, or species, of trees in the United States, all having many superficial features in common. To the casual observer, a tree is simply a tree. How then is it possible to recognize each species?

One can become skilled at identifying trees if he goes about the task in a scientific fashion. There are many features of trees which are of little value in recognition because they are not present in all trees of the species. The secret is to know what features to look for and which ones are reliable guides to the tree's identity. We can call these the "identification tags" of the tree. This means that you must develop the scientist's habit of careful observation of details which might be overlooked by a hit-or-miss approach.

At the outset you should be warned that very few trees can be accurately identified by their vegetative features alone. It is usually a combination of these with various reproductive structures which will enable you to be sure the tree is a sugar maple and not a Norway maple, or a red spruce and not a black spruce. Tree identification is fascinating, much like the task of a detective in tracking down people. He rarely relies on just a fingerprint, or the shape of a nose, or the color of hair. Each tree species, like every person, is a combination of certain features, all of which add up to that particular kind of tree.

The most important vegetative parts of the tree for purposes of tree recognition are the leaves, trunk, buds, and leaf-scars. The most important reproductive structures are the flowers (or cones) and the fruits. At various seasons of the year you will have to depend upon the organs which are then present; thus a knowledge of all the features which are typical of a particular kind of tree is necessary.

The General Appearance of Trees

We all know of certain trees which have such a distinctive appearance that they can readily be recognized by this alone. The growth pattern of the trunk and branches may result in an outline for the tree as a whole which makes recognition possible from a distance. This growth habit is determined by the location of the buds and the extent of their activity, resulting in three types of branching. In one type the stem produces buds only at its tip, none along its length. The result is a tall unbranched trunk with a cluster of leaves at the top, as in the palms. In a second type the stem produces buds along its length as well as at its tip but the growth of the terminal buds is more vigorous than that of the lateral buds which are to become the side branches. As a result the trunk elongates faster than the branches, producing a tall straight central axis supporting a cone-shaped mass of branches and foliage widest at the base and tapering to a pointed top. This type of growth prevails among the conifers and is well suited for

The three main types of tree growth are represented by the pyramid-shaped outline of a White Spruce (upper left), the columnar shape of a Cabbage Palm (upper right), and the hemispherical dome of a California Live Oak.

shedding ice and snow. Those who live in the northern states may have often noticed the tremendous weight of snow carried by the sloping foliage of a spruce or fir without injury to the tree.

A third type of branching results when the lateral buds grow at an equal rate to that of the terminal bud, or when the terminal bud is absent. In this case there is no main central trunk, once branching has begun. The foliage mass is broader than tall, resulting in a dome-shaped outline. Trees with this growth habit often are wider at the top than at the bottom, an excellent shape for intercepting the maximum amount of sunlight. In colder climates one handicap of this habit lies in the fact that when ice and snow accumulate on the branches, the load often splits the side branches from the main trunk. This hemispherical outline is common among the deciduous trees—thus maples, sycamores, and elms make excellent street and shade trees.

There are other variations in general appearance which a woodsman soon comes to recognize. White pine can be identified by the horizontal layering of the branches, Norway spruce by the drooping twigs and needles, and pitch pine by the twisted and scraggly growth. An old cypress of a southern swamp often has a typical flat-topped appearance as well as a buttressed base to its trunk. The red cedar of a New England field has a "tailored" cylindrical mass of foliage. Various deciduous trees also have individuality in their habit. The tulip tree can be recognized by its tall straight trunk and symmetrical branches; the dogwood by the arching upturned tips of the smaller branches; the American elm by its graceful vase-shaped outline.

It is surprising how many trees you can recognize in this way even when you see them from a distance or catch a quick glimpse of them from a car window. After becoming familiar with a tree at close range by leaf or flower features, walk a few hundred feet away and observe the tree as a whole. Its shape, or personality, can then become an additional "identification tag" the next time you meet it.

The Personality of Leaves

If our first exploration of a woodland trail is in summer in a region where both deciduous and evergreen trees grow, we soon discover that the most obvious difference between these two groups of trees is in the leaves. The leaf of a flowering tree (these make up almost all of the deciduous trees), like a maple or elm, is a fraction of an inch in thickness but may be twelve inches in length or breadth. The leaf of a conifer (and the majority of evergreen trees are conifers) is thicker and much narrower; it may be needle-like as in the pines, or in the form of small overlapping scales as in the cedars. Needles range in length from half an inch in the hemlock to fourteen inches in the pines; scale leaves are generally less than one eighth of an inch in length. There is little chance of confusing the leaves of these two kinds of trees. Therefore we can now consider in each group the details which are valuable as identification tags.

Variations in Types of Leaves.

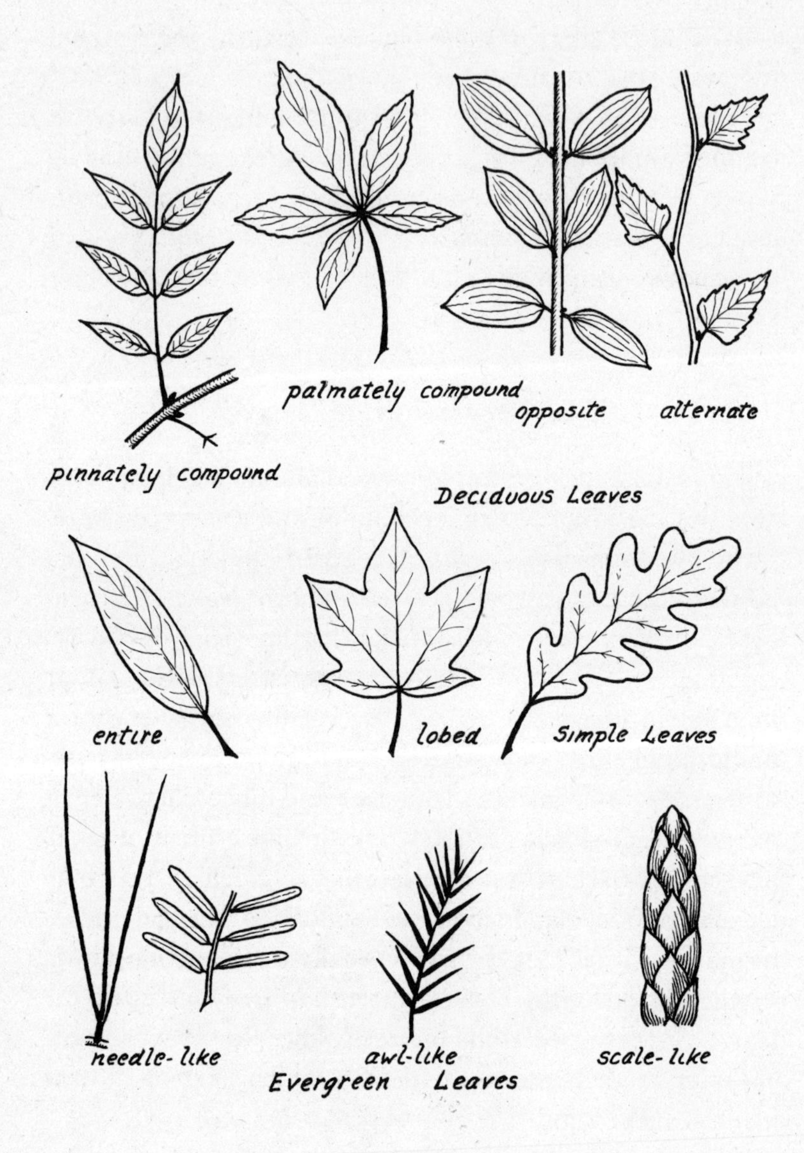

The variety of leaves which confronts us on a walk through deciduous woods undoubtedly will leave you much confused. It is possible however to learn certain short-cuts in recognizing trees by their leaves. Again it is a case of knowing what to look for. First of all, you should notice whether the leaf is all in one piece, even though it may be deeply indented along the margin, or whether it is subdivided into smaller leaflets. When a leaf is not divided into smaller sections it is called a *simple leaf*. Some common trees with simple leaves are the maples, poplars, birches, oaks, and elms. On the other hand the leaf may be composed of numerous small leaflets, in which case it is known as a *compound leaf*. Compound leaves are much larger than simple leaves, and are found on fewer kinds of trees. Familiar examples include the locusts, horse chestnut and buckeye, ailanthus, and pepper trees.

If for the moment we limit our observations to simple leaves, we discover a number of ways in which leaves of one species differ from those of another species. These important differences involve the outline of the leaf, its type of margin, and the method of arrangement on the stems and branches.

The outline of the leaf is a fairly reliable identification tag since, whether the leaf is large or small, young or old, it usually possesses a shape established by heredity for a particular species of tree. There are oblong, elliptical, rounded, heart-shaped and triangular leaves. They all have technical names which are useful to know when you are using any of the numerous tree manuals. Their shapes can best be remembered by seeing them; thus we can let the following illustration speak for itself.

Variations in Shape and Margins of Leaves.

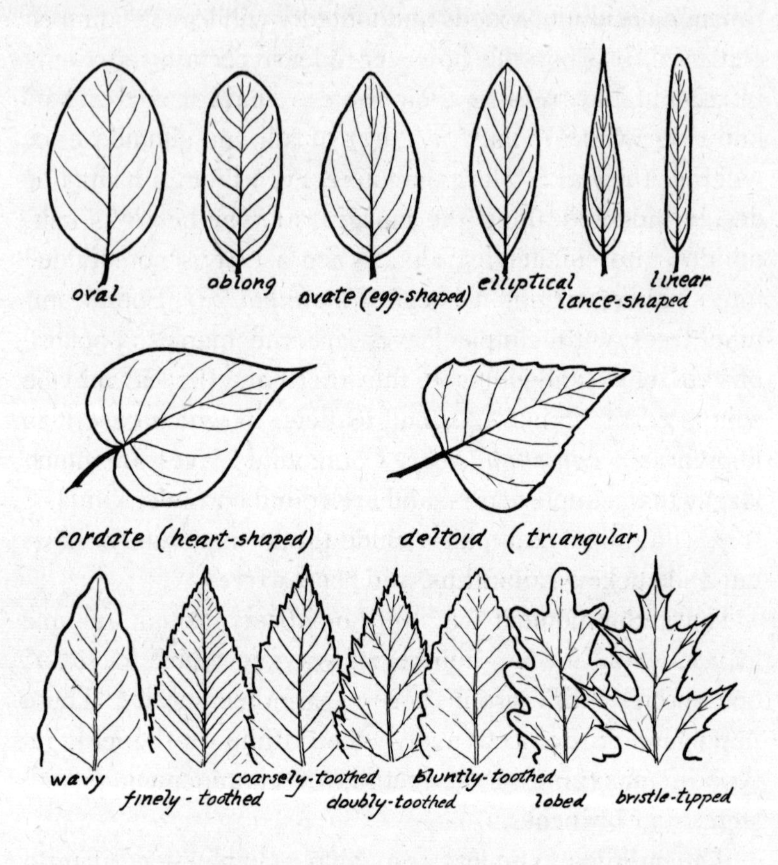

The appearance of the margin of the leaf is also fairly constant in the leaves of each kind of tree. As with leaf outlines, the leaf margins are described by special terms which need to be learned when you are consulting the more advanced tree guides. In general the margins may be entire (without any indentations) or variously toothed and lobed. In only a few cases are the trees confusing in having leaves with variable outlines and margins. Most notorious offenders in this respect are the sassafras and mulberry. The majority of trees are most cooperative, however, consistently retaining their individual leaf outline and type of margin.

The arrangement of leaves on the twig can sometimes be of assistance in identifying a tree. There are three types of leaf arrangement. In the alternate type, which is the most common, the leaves occur singly, attached first one to one side of the twig, then one to the other. Examples of alternate arrangement are found in the birches, poplars, and oaks. In the opposite arrangement the leaves grow in pairs, each attached to the twig just opposite another leaf. This is typical of the dogwood, maples, and ashes. Least common of all is the whorled pattern in which three or more leaves are attached to the stem at the same level; the catalpa has this type of leaf arrangement.

The actual size of the deciduous leaf is not a reliable guide because this varies with conditions affecting food manufacture and growth. Leaves of well-nourished sprout growth are sometimes four or five times larger than the leaves of mature trees of the same species. Size also varies with the age of the leaf, and its degree of exposure to the wind and sun. Among the cone-bearing trees the size of the leaves is a more constant feature and therefore can be used as an aid to identification; many of the pines can be tagged by the length of their needles. Another reliable feature to look for in the conifers is to note whether the needles are borne singly (hemlock and spruce) or in clusters (pine and larch).

Special Identification Features of Trunks

When trees are covered with foliage it usually is not necessary to notice stem and trunk features. However, as with the general habit of trees, it is worth while observing trunk peculiarities at the same time you are identifying the tree by its leaves. Then if you come across the tree in winter or any other time when it is leafless, you will be able to recognize it by the bark or other stem traits.

The trunks of young trees and the younger branches of old trees are generally not marked in such a way as to aid in identification. Many of them have a gray or brown smooth bark, sometimes tinged with green as in the aspen. This usually disappears as the tree grows older. In a few instances the trunk and branches bear telltale structures such as the warty outgrowths of the hackberry and the thorns of a locust or hawthorn. When the trunk becomes old, however, it may develop such distinctive features that they are worth remembering.

A few trees retain a smooth firm bark even when mature. The light gray bark of a beech is a familiar sight in northeastern woodlands, as is the darker gray bark of the holly and magnolia farther south. The yellowish bark of an aspen and the shiny red bark of a young cherry are easily remembered. In some trees the bark is distinguished by horizontal markings, or lenticels, which act as breathing pores for the trunk. The lenticels are rounded and coarse in the cherries and poplars, but in the birches they form thin horizontal lines extending around the trunk. The paper birch is perhaps the easiest tree to recognize by its bark.

Bark becomes a valuable identification tag of mature trees. (Upper row) Norway Maple, White Pine; (middle row) Eucalyptus, Honey Locust; (lower row) Sycamore, White Birch.

Then there are the trees whose bark is furrowed and ridged in a definite pattern. White ash and Norway maple have firmly and smoothly ridged bark, as has the tulip tree. The bark of a sugar maple looks as if a small plow had been run up and down the trunk, producing furrows with overturned edges. In some pines the bark is broken into squarish plates and scaly sections. Smaller rectangular plates give an alligator-skin design to dogwood bark. The stately incense cedar and redwood have trunks with fluted and deeply-furrowed patterns in the bark.

In other trees the bark is shredded and torn into threads and strips. Red cedar bark separates in stringy sections. The eucalyptus trunk is often covered with hanging shreds of bark torn partially loose from the lighter-color bark underneath. Shagbark hickory has loose plates of bark attached by their middle to the underlying tissue. Sycamore, another tree with an easily recognized bark, loses irregular patches of its dark brown outer bark to reveal the yellowish and white bark underneath.

Cones, Catkins and Flowers

Botanists who make a study of identifying plants accurately for research purposes usually look for reproductive structures as undisputed evidence for the identity of the plant with which they are dealing. Unfortunately reproductive organs are frequently absent, or hard to secure. For the young naturalist they present the added drawback of being more difficult to understand.

In the cone-bearing group it is the egg-producing (and therefore the seed producing) cone which is the identifica-

The seed-producing cones of conifers are reliable recognition features. Above, White Spruce; below, Hemlock and Douglas Spruce.

Poplar catkins are representative of the tassel-like flower clusters of poplars, birches, and oaks.

tion tag for the tree. These cones, if not attached to the branches, can usually be found on the ground beneath the tree. Cones are very satisfactory recognition features of all the conifers because their variations in size, shape and nature of the cone scales indicate the different species. Cones vary in size from the inch-long structures of hemlock and larch to the twenty-inch cones of the sugar pine.

Some of the flowering trees produce inconspicuous flowers in tassel or cone-like clusters known as catkins. The small flowers are usually green or yellow, and lack petals and sepals. For this reason the average person does not think of them as flowers. The most familiar catkin is the "pussy" of a pussy willow. Tassel-like catkins occur on poplars and birches. In the oaks and hickories only the pollen-producing flowers are in the catkins, the egg-bearing flowers being formed in special structures which become nuts and acorns. Although a catkin is actually a cluster of small wind-pollinated flowers, these are so different from the ordinary idea of a flower that for our purposes we can consider the catkin-bearing trees to be in a special group by themselves.

On the other hand many trees produce flowers which are so like the common types found in woods and gardens that they are readily recognized as flowers. This is because they have the brightly colored sepals or petals which attract attention to the flower. These are the trees which bring beauty to the woods and hillsides in spring, and are planted as prized ornamentals around our homes.

Two groups of flowering trees are easily identified by the similarity of their flowers to their more familiar garden relatives; these are the trees in the rose and pea families. A wild rose flower consists of five equally-proportioned sepals and five similarly shaped petals. Some common trees with typical rose flowers, since they all belong in the rose family, are shadbush, hawthorns, black cherry, and chokecherry.

The pea flower is distinctive in having fused sepals which form a tube with an upper and a lower lip, surrounding the five unequal-sized petals. The uppermost petal is large, the two side petals are smaller, and the two lowermost petals form an upturned keel. This type is best seen in the cultivated sweet pea. Some common trees in the pea family are redbud, honey locust, black locust, and mimosa.

Other trees than those in the rose and pea families have

conspicuous and brightly colored blossoms. The large waxy white flowers of the magnolia sometimes reach a diameter of eight inches. Horse chestnut, buckeye, and catalpa are well known for their showy erect clusters of white flowers. The princess tree of the southeastern states has erect clusters of pale blue blossoms. Perhaps most prized of all the native flowering trees is the dogwood; in this tree the flowers are small, in yellow clusters, but are surrounded by showy spreading white bracts.

The remaining flowering trees, which have neither catkins nor showy flowers of typical structure, produce flowers of small size and generally inconspicuous colors. Among them are found the elms, ashes, linden, sycamore, and some maples. In many of these trees the flowers lack

The small clusters of yellow Dogwood flowers are surrounded by showy white bracts.

petals and sepals, consisting only of the essential pollen and egg-producing organs. Most showy of this group is the red maple, whose crimson flower clusters add color to the otherwise drab woods at an early period in spring, when most trees have as yet not thought of awakening from their winter's sleep.

Fruits as Identification Tags

Many trees produce fruits which are large and conspicuous enough to be distinguishing features, especially after the leaves have fallen. Some of these are suited for wind dispersal by having structures which enable them to be carried a considerable distance and thus give their enclosed seeds a chance at germinating in new territory. Other fruits are adapted for dispersal by birds and mammals; they are usually brightly colored and fleshy in contrast with the browns and grays of the dry wind-dispersed fruits.

Wind-dispersed fruits are generally small and provided with papery wings or parachutes which aid them in sailing through the air. Few children grow up without having collected the winged "key" fruits of the maples. Also provided with winged projections are the fruits of ash and ailanthus. The linden has an interesting sail-like bract attached to the stem of the fruit cluster, and the rounded nutlet of the elm is surrounded by a papery rim.

Nuts and acorns are large-seeded fruits of the hickory and oak trees. There are many different species of oaks in various parts of the country, many of them difficult to identify by their leaves alone. In most cases the acorns of each species are sufficiently different to be of great use in identifying the trees of this group. It is hardly necessary to make any reference to the differences in appearance of walnuts, butternuts, hickory nuts and pecans. The beech has a prickly fruit enclosing several small triangular seeds; the chestnut, once very common along the Atlantic Coast, has a larger prickly bur enclosing the chestnuts. Horse chestnut and buckeye produce large spherical capsules containing the nuts.

Elongated pods and pod-like fruits are typical of several common trees. The honey locust has large brown twisted pods up to ten or twelve inches in length; they hang on the branches long after the leaves have fallen. Common locust pods are smaller and lighter in color. Catalpa branches are often decorated for most of the winter months with pods eight to ten inches in length which give the tree its common name of Indian bean.

Ball-like fruit clusters readily identify three common trees of eastern United States: the sweet gum, sycamore, and osage orange. Sweet gum fruits are balls of capsules with projecting tips, creating a spiny appearance. Sycamore balls are larger and made up of tightly packed wind-dispersed fruits. Largest of all is the green fruit of the osage orange, reaching a diameter of five inches and made up of many fused small fleshy fruits; this aptly-named "orange" has a spicy and aromatic odor.

The most typical fleshy fruits are the berry-like ones produced by the trees of the rose family and a few other groups of trees. Shadbush has dark blue or purple berries; mountain ash produces hanging clusters of brilliant scarlet berries; and hawthorns in autumn are covered with

Fruits, when present, are another reliable identification tag of trees. Left, pods of the Royal Poinciana; right, fleshy fruit of the Osage Orange.

bright red berries which resemble small apples. In autumn the dogwood branches are also decorated with bright red fruits. On the Pacific Coast, the pepper tree is known for its hanging clusters of bright red berries.

It is unfortunate that this description of tree personalities has had to be an arm-chair exploration trip. It would have been much better if we could have made the same observations while looking at the actual trees as we encountered them on a walk through the woods. But perhaps you and your friends can take such a walk or perhaps your family may take a vacation trip to the lakes or the mountains. If so, you should be able to discover a few of the traits which make tree identification easy and interesting.

The northern forest, as in this New Hampshire scene, is often dominated by Red Spruce.

Chapter 3

THE FOREST AS A TREE COMMUNITY

TREES with a preference for similar living conditions tend to associate with each other, just as people with similar interests and occupations congregate into villages and towns. The place where a plant or animal lives is known as its *habitat,* a special kind of environment with definite food relationships, temperature variations, rainfall and soil. Several kinds of trees with the same habitat form a natural community, in the same way that a village or city is a community of people.

This is common knowledge to anyone who has traveled through various sections of the country. In almost every state sheltered valleys, swampy hollows, shaded ravines and exposed ridges offer a variety of habitats for tree growth. The fertile valley soil may support as its community a woodland of sugar maple, beech, elm, and linden. The swampy lowland may be a tangled growth of red maple, tamarack, yellow birch and black spruce. The coolness and moisture of the shaded ravine habitat may encourage a community of hemlock and beech trees. On the dry rocky ridges the community may include the more hardy pitch pines, hickories and oaks. The particular community in which a tree usually is found thus becomes another aid to tree identification, for when the preferred habitat of a tree is known you can expect to find it in certain places, and not in others.

These small communities generally live in restricted areas, and are determined by soil, drainage, amount of shade and other local conditions. They group themselves, however, into larger communities just as villages and towns form states. These larger groups have their distribution determined by widespread climatic conditions, which are chiefly the amount of rainfall or snowfall, and the annual temperature variations. The latter is important because it determines the length of the growing season. A forest is such a large community, made up of trees with similar climate preferences.

If you have crossed the country from coast to coast, or north and south from the Great Lakes to the Gulf of Mexico, you probably have noticed several types of forest communities. Actually there are six of them. They are the northern forest of New England and the Great Lakes states, the deciduous forest of the central states, the southern forest of the Atlantic coastal plain, the Rocky Mountain forest, and the Pacific Coast forest. The sixth and most unusual forest type is the tropical forest of the southern tip of Florida.

It is obvious that if we know what trees belong to any one of the above forest communities and what species are excluded from it, we can eliminate, in identifying an unknown tree, many species which are not likely to grow in that particular geographic region or habitat. As an example, if we discover a strange pine while exploring the woods of Massachusetts or Connecticut, we can be quite certain it is not any one of the four common pines of the southern forest, or of the pines of the Rocky Mountain and Pacific Coast forests. This narrows it down to one of the four native pines of the northern forest. In other words, trees do not occur in a haphazard fashion throughout our forty-eight states. They have definite geographic homes, and definite habitats within that range.

Why Trees Grow Where They Do

Trees, like all plants, are born with an inherited preference for certain habitats because they possess structures and carry on activities suitable for living best in one kind of environment. This special fitness for living in a particular sort of place keeps them, at the same time, from spreading into other habitats. The environment provides a certain combination of living conditions which affect the tree's photosynthesis, growth and reproductive habits. Some of these conditions are determined by the climate: air temperature, amount of sunlight, atmospheric humidity and rainfall. Others are associated with the mineral composition and physical nature of the soil. Still others are correlated with the presence (or absence) of other plants, of animals and of man.

Every woodsman knows that willows and sycamores indicate the nearness of water, that hemlocks prefer shaded moist hillsides, that red cedar is common in open fields and that cypress grows in southern swamplands. He looks for evergreens, such as spruce and fir, near timber line on high eastern mountains and for elm in well-watered lowland valleys. The needle type of leaf enables its posesssor to grow in the range of the northern and western forests, where the broad-leaved trees are at a disadvantage. The jack and pitch pines will grow on poor rocky and sandy soil where the white pine, with its requirement of richer soil, cannot grow. These and many other observations on trees reveal that trees have a reason for growing where they do.

The forest community may be entirely made up of conifers, it may be exclusively an association of deciduous trees, or it may be a combination of both. In regions of rigorous winters, cool summers, and a short growing season the forest is likely to be an evergreen one, a community of conifers with a hereditary ability to grow in such an environment. Farther south, evergreen forests occur where the soil is generally too poor to support a deciduous growth.

Heavy forest growth is found in the eastern third of the United States, where there is adequate rainfall throughout the year to support tree growth. As we travel westward from the Atlantic Coast we see the forests dwindling in extent, the trees becoming smaller and smaller, until finally the woods disappear and the prairie grasses take over. In the United States the rainfall decreases as one goes inland from each coast in an east-west direction. A north-south line from the Dakotas to southeastern Texas indicates the western limit of an annual rainfall of twenty inches or more. This also marks the treeless belt of the country, since an annual rainfall of less than twenty inches generally eliminates the possibility of natural forest growth, except along stream margins.

West of the prairies, tree growth returns in the foothills and along the lower slopes of the Rocky Mountains. Here the altitude and increased rainfall or snowfall provides the suitable habitat for a large forest community. West of the Rockies the desert basins again have too little

Eastern Forest Communities.

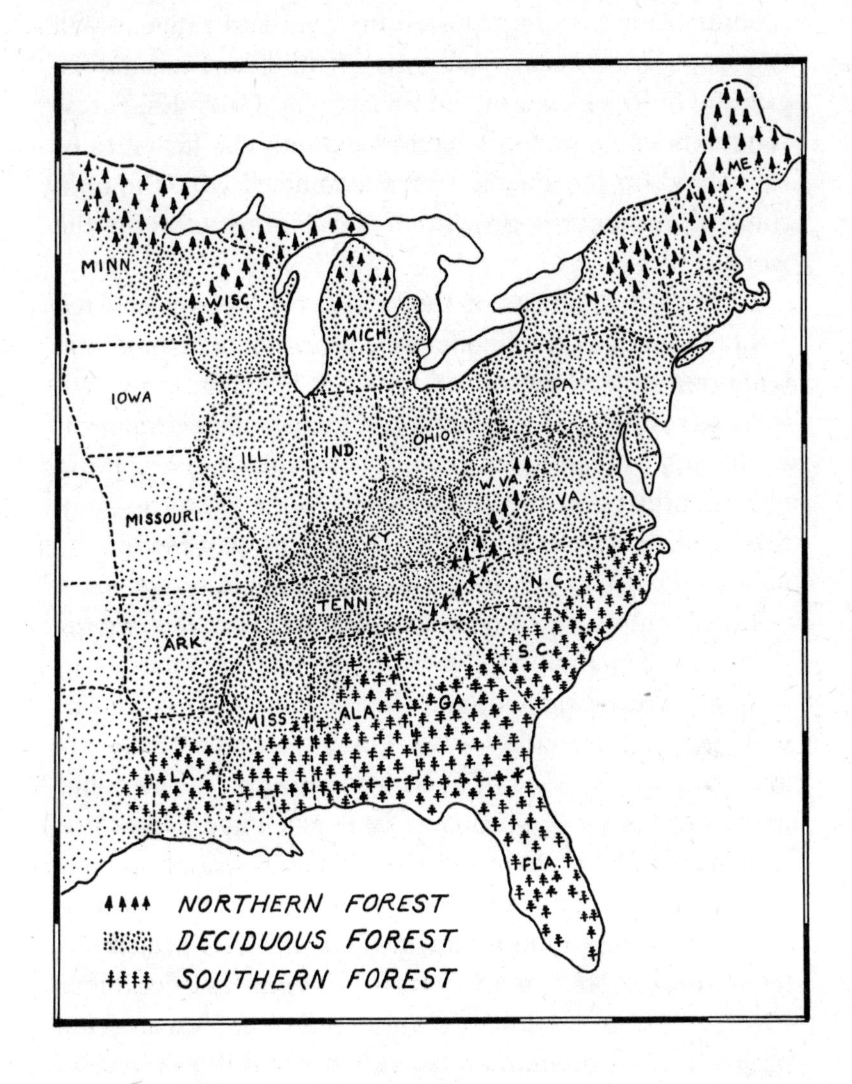

precipitation for development of forest communities, although at higher elevations on the scattered ranges small groups of trees occur. But west of the desert basins, beginning on the slopes of the Sierras and Cascades, forest communities appear in generous extent. The heavy rainfall found on the Pacific Coast, combined with the mild climate, encourages growth of the largest trees in the world.

The original forests of the United States once covered a total area of 820 million acres, nearly half of our total land area. After several centuries of population growth with its resulting agricultural and industrial development, about 495 million acres remain. In spite of the popular idea that the great forest regions lie in the western states, three-quarters of our forests are found today east of the plains states, mostly east of the Mississippi River.

Long cold winters and short summers characterize the region surrounding the Great Lakes, upper New York, northern New England, and the mountainous Appalachians extending south to the Great Smokies. Here we find the *northern forest,* in which conifers are the dominant trees. A large portion of central United States is a region of milder winters, longer summers, and suitable soil conditions for deciduous tree growth. This is therefore the range of the great *deciduous forest* which extends throughout twenty states. Between this deciduous forest and the Atlantic Ocean, east of the Appalachian highlands, is the *southern forest,* where conifers thrive in the abundant rainfall and long growing season, but in soil too poor for agriculture.

Extending somewhat diagonally northwest to southeast

Western Forest Communities.

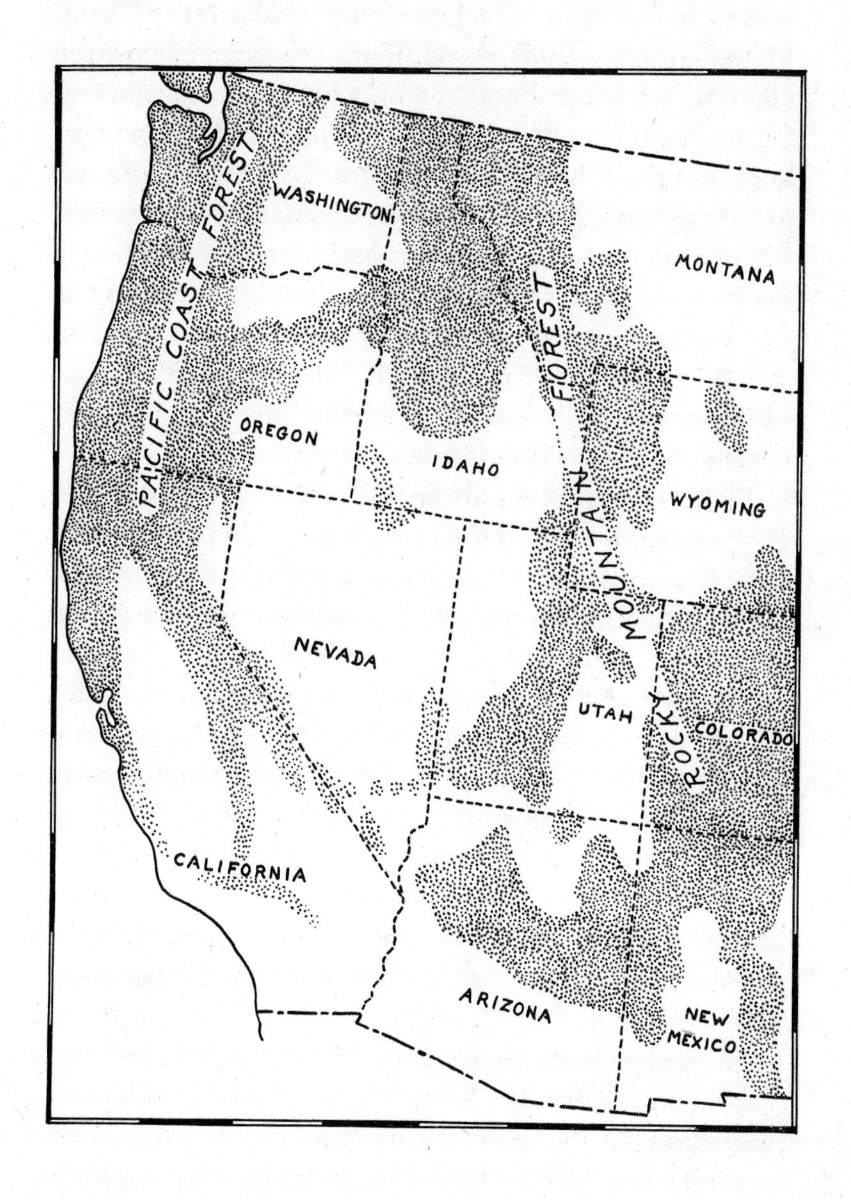

from Canada to Mexico is a great jumble of plateaus, peaks, and mountain ranges which make up the Rocky Mountains. Here living conditions are much like those of the northern forest area, and only hardy evergreens and a few deciduous trees make up the forest community known as the *Rocky Mountain forest.* Pines, spruces and firs are abundant in this forest as they are in the northern forest, but they are different species from those in the northeastern states. The *Pacific forest,* thriving on the far western mountains and along the Pacific Coast, is a mixed community of conifer and broad-leaved trees, but of different species from those of the East. It is the most heavily wooded region in the country.

These forests are the original homes of our native trees. In many states the original continuous forest has disappeared and the surviving trees are left as lonely individuals or small groups amid the numerous agricultural and city areas. In many states, too, you will find that the forests do not maintain clear boundaries, but grade into other forest types because local conditions favor growth of more than one forest community. Thus, if you should wish to follow a forest trail in pure northern forest you would have to select the mountainous or northern part of New England and New York, or the summits of the mountains in Tennessee and the Carolinas. On the other hand, a forest trail in typical deciduous forest would most likely have to be in Ohio, Indiana or Kentucky. These two forest types merge in the lowlands of New England and New York, and in much of Pennsylvania; hence if your trails lead through the woods of this region you will be likely to meet trees from both the northern forest and the deciduous forest. In Maryland and Virginia, just to complicate matters for the naturalist, you are likely to find not only trees from these two forest types but also from the southern forest!

The Northern Forest

Almost all of the common trees found in New England, New York, the Great Lakes states, and adjacent areas are natives of the northern forest. The dominant trees are spruces, pines and balsam firs; the larch, a conifer which sheds its needles every winter, is also a member of this forest. Deciduous trees mingle with these conifers or grow in pure stands by themselves. Among these species are the birches, maples and aspens. If you live in Maine, New Hampshire, Vermont, northern New York, Minnesota, Wisconsin or Michigan, your woodland wanderings are likely to lead into the habitats of these trees.

The rigorous climate of this region includes long winters, during which a groundcover of snow many feet thick prevents deep-freezing of the soil. As a result tree growth is possible which would be lacking if the uncovered soil were frozen deeply. The short cool summers provide ideal vacation spots but handicap the trees by limiting their growing season. About 83 million acres are covered by this northern forest. The White Mountain National Forest and Great Smokies National Park are two recreational areas in this region. To a lesser degree, the northern forest is represented in Acadia National Park and the Green Mountain National Forest and in the Adirondacks State Park.

The Deciduous Forest

This is the largest, and also the most diverse, community of deciduous trees in the United States. The annual rainfall in this area varies from twenty-five to sixty inches; the temperature is milder during winter and the snowfall less, than in the region of the northern forest. The distribution of rainfall throughout the year is ideal for growth of deciduous trees. The soil is richer, too, as is evident from the agricultural value of the cleared land. The growing season is much longer, ranging from five to eight months. This forest community covers an area of 132 million acres.

In the northeastern portion of this forest the dominant trees are maples, birches, beech, pine and hemlock. Also typical of this part of the deciduous forest are elms, ashes, linden and some oaks and hickories. If you live in southern New England or New York, the lowlands of Pennsylvania, or southern Michigan, Wisconsin and Minnesota, your forest trails will lead through communities of these trees.

A more central portion includes the same maples and birches found farther north, but in addition are found more species of oaks and hickories. Sweet gum, tulip tree and black walnut are also common members of this forest. Those of you who live in Maryland, Virginia, West Virginia, Ohio, Indiana or the lowlands of Kentucky and Tennessee are familiar with this forest.

From Minnesota on the north to Texas on the south, the western front of this deciduous forest is made up of oak-hickory woods in which the individual trees are

The deciduous forest of our central states is frequently a mixture of oak, beech, and maple.

smaller than those in the forests farther east. Often they form open park-like groves. If you live in southern Illinois, Iowa, Missouri or Arkansas, your woodland explorations will lead into the homes of these trees.

The Southern Forest

This large forest region, covering 149 million acres, is found in the coastal plain and Gulf states from North Carolina to Texas. The sandy and generally poor soil which is typical of most of this region can support an evergreen forest of only those trees which tolerate such soil and drainage conditions. The abundant rainfall, mild winters and long growing season contribute to produce even better conditions for forest growth than are found in the central states. In the southern forest many trees of great commercial value are produced.

The dominant trees are pines. To the visitor driving south along the Atlantic Coast, the pine forests present an almost unbroken tree community for hundreds of miles. From the pines of this area are secured most of the turpentine and rosin of the world and one-third of all the lumber cut in the United States. In the lowlands and swamps grow bald cypress, sweet gum and red maple.

An interesting community within this southern forest is the *hammock,* an area of broad-leaved evergreen trees, mainly magnolia, bay and live oak. Scattered groves of cabbage palms lend a tropical appearance to the coastal forests from South Carolina to Florida. The ever-present Spanish moss, an air plant of the pineapple family, drapes many of the forest trees with streamers of gray-green.

The climatic and soil conditions which determine the distribution of the three eastern forest communities do not form clear-cut boundaries and certainly do not coincide with state lines. As a result, in many of the eastern states a wooded area may include a mixture of trees from these forests, depending upon altitude and local variations in rainfall and temperature. These "in-between" areas are especially common in southern New England and New York, Pennsylvania, New Jersey, Maryland and Virginia. In these states we may be confronted with such northern trees as white pine and red spruce; central plains trees such as various nut trees, oaks, osage orange and dogwood; and southern trees such as redbud and holly.

This makes it difficult to predict exactly what trees may be found in these states. However, at least one thing you can be certain of. With the exception of the aspen poplar, balsam poplar and white spruce, few of the native trees of the eastern forests occur in the Pacific and Rocky Mountain forests.

The Rocky Mountain Forest

Extending for thirteen hundred miles across western United States, roughly from northwest to southeast in the Rocky Mountains, is a forest region of many disconnected communities, totalling 63 million acres. The trees are almost all evergreens, since these are the only species which can survive the short growing season, long cold winters, strong winds and heavy snowfall. The forests begin at about 5,000 feet altitude and, in the southern Rockies, reach timber line at 12,000 feet. Below them are the sloping prairies and the desert basins where tree growth is very sparse. Western species of spruce, fir and pine make up the greater part of this forest community. The deciduous trees are mainly aspens, oaks, cottonwoods and sycamores.

The change in the forest population is very striking as one drives up a mountain such as Pikes Peak. Ponderosa pine forms great forests at the 5,000 to 6,000 foot altitudes. Farther up the Douglas fir and white fir join the ponderosa pine, while at about 8,000 feet the pines disappear and the firs form a pure stand. These in turn give way at higher altitudes to Engelmann spruce, finally at timber line another change taking place, with alpine fir replacing the spruce.

The Rocky Mountain forest occupies western Montana, most of Idaho, western Wyoming, and all the elevated plateaus of Utah, Colorado, Arizona and New Mexico. Many of our most popular national parks lie in this forest region: Glacier, Yellowstone, Grand Teton, Rocky Mountain, Mesa Verde, Zion, Bryce Canyon and Grand Canyon National Parks owe some of their recreational value to the tree members of this forest community.

The Pacific Coast Forest

From the Canadian border to central California, and from the Pacific Coast to the Sierras and Cascades, lies another large evergreen forest, comprising 66 million acres of the most valuable timber resources of the country. Douglas fir makes up almost half of the entire acreage, pure stands of these trees extending for hundreds of miles in Oregon and Washington. Western species of pine dominate the remaining half of the area, but some western species of hemlock and cedar are also found in this forest. At its southern edge, in Oregon and California, grow the famous species of Sequoia, occupying a million and a half acres.

Well known national parks lie in the Pacific Coast forest: Mount Rainier, Crater Lake, Yosemite and Sequoia National Parks.

These are the native homes of our American trees. If nature were left to herself, each of the trees belonging to one of these forest communities would be found only in that region or its adjacent areas, and nowhere else. But man has seen fit to introduce these trees from one part of the country to another, such as the blue spruce from Colorado to New England, and the redbud from the Carolinas to Connecticut. Man has also destroyed many forest regions and replaced them by agricultural lands, introducing foreign trees for crops or ornamental purposes.

In the following chapters the trees will be described as part of their original community, although today these trees may have been transplanted to many states remote from their native home.

Red Pines, like these at Lake Chocorua, New Hampshire, often provide tempting picnic and camping sites.

Chapter 4

TRAILS IN THE NORTHERN FOREST

MANY TREES of our northern forest occur also in the land to the north of us and thus represent a southward extension of Canadian species suited to live in our cooler states. Some of these Canadian trees range across the entire breadth of the continent from Nova Scotia to Alaska. It is not surprising, therefore, to find these trees crossing the Canadian boundary into Minnesota, Wisconsin and Michigan as well as into New York and New England. In fact a few of them also come into the United States in the Rocky Mountain region.

This group of tree neighbors of the North includes the white, red and jack pines; the white, red and black spruces; balsam fir and eastern larch. Hardy deciduous trees are represented by the willows, aspens and birches.

Mingling with them are those more southern and central species which have ventured north and east in search of living space. Pitch pine and red cedar are conifers of this group. Various other species of birch and maple, together with sycamore, elm and cherry, have joined this forest community.

We are likely to meet these trees as we explore the woods of Acadia National Park or roam along the northern coast of Maine, in the numerous climbs which invite the hiker in the White Mountains of New Hampshire and the Green Mountains of Vermont, in the Berkshires of Massachusetts and the Adirondacks of New York. Farther south we can find the same trees at higher altitudes in the mountains of Maryland and Pennsylvania and farthest south of all in the high ridges of the Great Smoky Mountains of North Carolina and Tennessee. At increased altitude, living conditions are similar to those of lower elevations farther north. For this reason we find red spruce which grows at sea level in Maine thriving at six thousand feet elevation in North Carolina. Isolated outposts of the northern forest clothe the summit of Mt. Mitchell (6,684 feet), which is the highest mountain east of the Mississippi River.

Conditions favorable to the growth of all these trees are not likely to be found along any one particular forest trail. Thus it will be necessary to take an imaginary walk in which various species of related trees are all conveniently growing together. This will make it easier to learn their "identification tags" but is, of course, an artificial arrangement. Some of these trees in nature are never found growing with each other since they prefer different habitats.

The Pines

Few people realize, unless they have traveled widely, how common pine trees are in the United States. They are as much a part of the landscape in Virginia or Alabama as in New England; they are as familiar to one who lives in Minnesota as to a resident of the Carolinas. Pines are conspicuous members of the forests in the Rockies and along the Pacific Coast. Wherever trees grow, in fact, pines usually have their representatives in the forest family. Thus when you become familiar with the pines you will feel at home in practically every state.

All pines can be recognized by their evergreen foliage, which consists of long slender needle-like leaves in clusters of two or more. Theirs is a less pyramid-shaped outline than that of the spruces and firs, and the branches of a pine generally extend horizontally or spread upward

Pines of the Northern Forest.

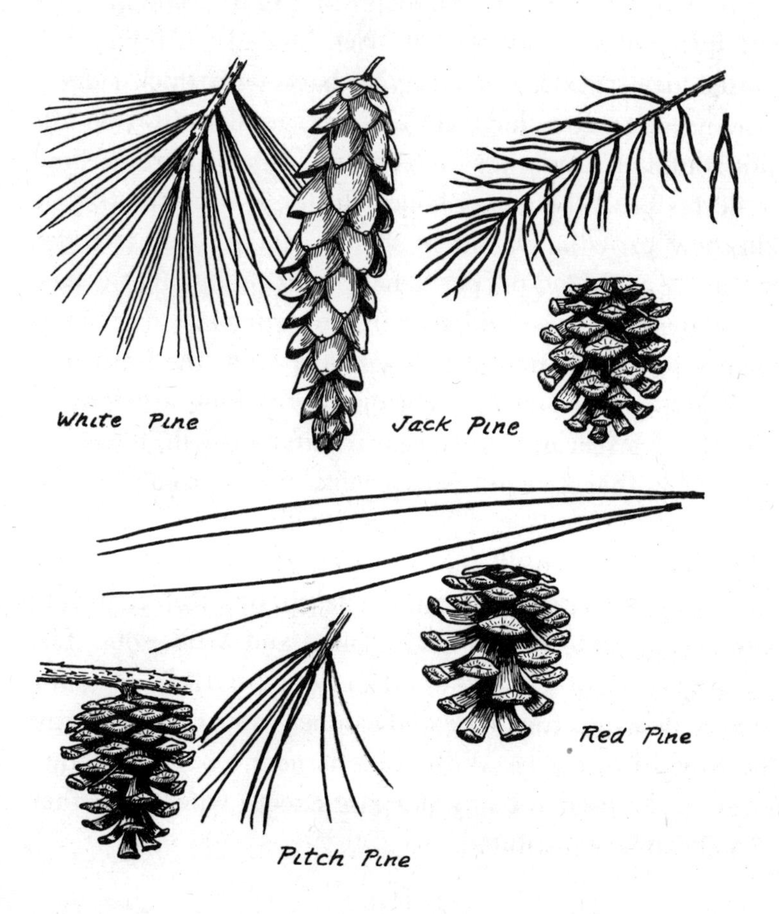

rather than droop toward the ground. The only other conifer with needles in clusters is the larch, but its needles are soft and short by comparison and occur in rosettes of a dozen or more needles. In winter the two cannot be confused since the larch is deciduous. Pines have long tap roots, which make them difficult to transplant from the woods. Thus it is wise to resist that impulse to dig up an attractive pine seedling. It is wiser to buy a nursery-grown pine which will have a much better chance of surviving.

WHITE PINE, from a distance, can be recognized by the horizontal layering of its rich blue-green foliage. A closer view reveals firm grayish bark with thick ridges. The needles grow in clusters of *five,* an identification tag not found on any other eastern pine. Small bright-yellow male (pollen producing) cones cluster around the tips of the new growth. On other shoots of the same tree develop the pink and purple female (egg-producing) cones. They mature the second year into brown cones five to ten inches in length, hanging downward from the branches.

Young white pines grow rapidly, reaching a height of twenty-five feet in twenty years. Later growth, however, is so slow that it requires two centuries to produce a tree four feet in diameter. The largest white pine on record is growing near Newald in Forest County, Wisconsin. It has a circumference of 17 feet and a height of 140 feet. White pine is the state tree of both Maine and Minnesota. The creamy straight-grained wood has long been a favorite for doors, flooring, furniture and cabinet work because it can be worked so easily. White pine is now too scarce, however, to be used for any purpose except where no other wood can be substituted.

RED PINE, like white pine, is rarely found today in pure stands except in remote regions of Minnesota and other Great Lakes states. Known also as Norway pine, this handsome species can be recognized from a distance by its straight tall central trunk with warm reddish-brown bark, and by the luster of the glossy green foliage. Red pine reaches its best growth on the sandy plains but it also thrives on dry gravelly ridges. It cannot be confused with any other native northeastern pine because its long flexible needles grow *two* in a cluster. The introduced Austrian pine also has two needles in a cluster but it is found only in or near inhabited areas as a cultivated tree.

In late spring clusters of small purple male cones are found on the lower branches; higher up on the tree the scarlet seed-producing cones appear. Like those of the white pine, the seed cone takes two years to mature, growing into a brown cone about two inches in length. Most of the red pines, scattered through the forest community, are sixty to seventy feet in height with a trunk diameter of a few feet. A few trees have been reported to reach a height of over a hundred feet. The wood, heavier than that of white pine, is often sold with it. One special virtue of red pine lies in its thick bark which is resistant to fire; thus the tree is not as easily injured in this way as is white pine. Red pine, since it also survives transplanting more easily, is a favored species for reforestation and ornamental planting.

JACK PINE is also a two-needled pine like the red pine, but it would be difficult to confuse the two species. Jack pine is generally a scraggly and dwarfed tree with twisted branches and yellowish or brownish green foliage.

Under best conditions, as in Minnesota, it grows to be a slender tall tree sixty feet or more in height. It is uncommon in New England, but can be found in Acadia National Park and adjacent coastal headlands. Here the jack pine, rarely more than twenty feet tall, grows on rocky slopes where few other pines will venture.

Also known as Banks' pine, gray pine and northern scrub pine, this species has the distinction of being one of the most northern of all pines. It advances to within a few hundred miles of the Arctic Circle, and ranges from Hudson Bay to British Columbia. For all its unkempt appearance, jack pine serves a useful purpose in pioneering into areas which have been burned over, or after lumber operations, providing humus and shelter for the seedlings of the more useful trees which succeed it.

The twisted pairs of needles are the shortest of any eastern pine, rarely being more than an inch and a half in length. The unusual cones are incurved and lop-sided, apparently clinging to the branch along their entire length. The weak brittle wood is of little use, but with the growing scarcity of other pines it is being cut to furnish lumber for packing cases, crates and barrels.

PITCH PINE, like the jack pine, is a low-growing tree, often grotesquely-branched, adding an unusual touch to the landscape. Close observation reveals that the foliage consists of clusters with *three* needles; since no other northeastern pine has this number of needles in a cluster, pitch pine can be readily identified by this means. Its usual habitat is a sandy plain, or on the slopes of rocky ridges and hillsides.

Short stiff needles, averaging three inches in length, are sharply pointed and spread outwards at sharp angles from the twigs. The seed-producing cones reach a length of several inches, the cone scales opening in fall and winter to scatter the winged brown seeds—a welcome feast for squirrels, quail and various winter bird residents. The soft-grained wood is too pitchy to be of much lumber value; however, pitch pine shows a remarkable resistance to fire, has few other enemies and can grow under very adverse soil conditions. An unusually large specimen at Middleburg, New York, has a circumference of 8 feet and a height of 70 feet.

The Spruces

The spruces form another large group of evergreens frequently encountered as we explore forest trails in the northeastern states. Of thirty-eight species which grow in the colder portions of the northern hemisphere, seven are native to the United States and three of these occur in the northern forest community. Spruces are hardy trees, reaching the shores of Hudson Bay and northern Alaska. They also march up the sides of the eastern mountains, becoming the last of the trees to yield to the elements at timber line. When growing in the open they can be recognized by their symmetrical pyramid-shaped outline and the branches growing out at regular intervals in whorls from the straight main trunk. Spruce needles are shorter than those of the pines and grow singly along the twigs, pointing outwards in all directions and thus giving a "bottle-brush" effect to the foliage. Each needle is four-angled and sharply pointed; thus it is a prickly experience to force one's way through a spruce thicket.

RED SPRUCE is the most common eastern spruce, forming solid stands along our northeastern seacoasts and inland thickets, and growing in close ranks along the upper slopes of the mountains. It generally is found on well-drained soil where there is a continuous and abundant water supply. The largest red spruce on record is grow-

Other Needle-leaved Trees of the Northern Forest.

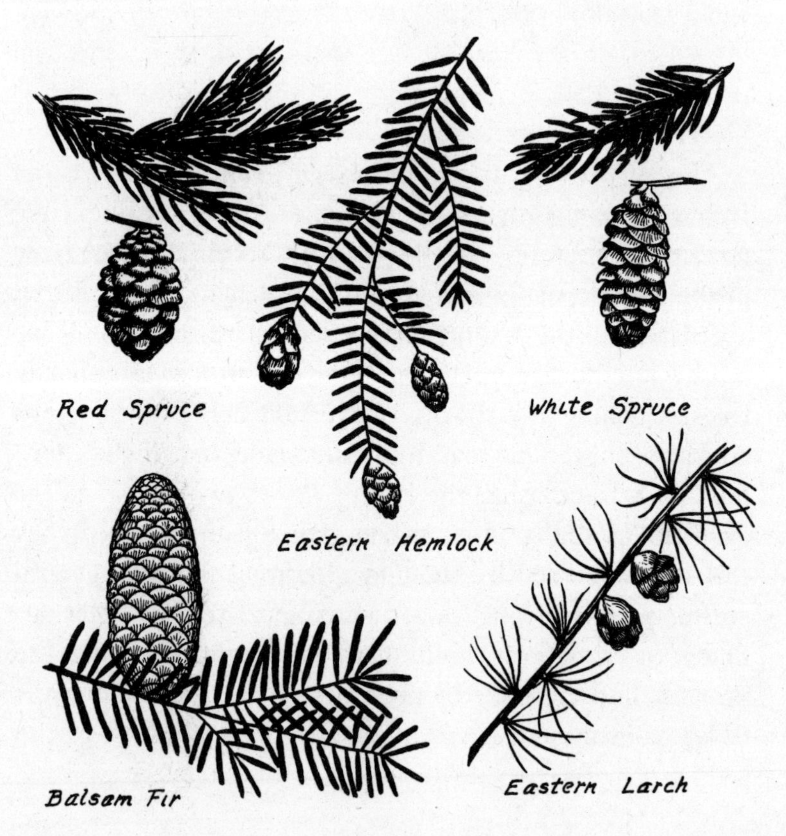

ing in Great Smoky Mountains National Park; it has a circumference of 14 feet and a height of 75 feet.

The yellowish-green foliage consists of crowded needles, each about half an inch in length, clothing the twigs on all sides. Trunks of old trees have a dark reddish-brown bark covered with flaking scales. The bright red small male cones appear early in spring on the lower branches; seed-producing cones develop on other branches near the tops of the tree. They are cylindrical and reddish-green when young, erect until they have been pollinated. After pollination the cones hang downward, maturing later the same year and changing from a purplish to a reddish-brown color. They are several inches in length when full grown. Red squirrels and chipmunks prize the seeds, as do crossbills and pine siskins.

Spruce wood is strong and used for rough lumber, but its greatest importance lies in its value as paper pulp. Red spruce furnishes a large share of the pulpwood of the East because of its long, straight, light-colored fibers. Thousands of cords of neatly piled spruce pulpwood line the back roads of northern New England every spring, the trees being cut in winter. Red spruce is also used as a Christmas tree although it is not as popular for this purpose as balsam fir.

WHITE SPRUCE ranges from the Hudson Bay-Alaska region southward into Montana, the Great Lakes states, and the New York-New England region. It is one of the few conifers which grows wild in both eastern and western United States. White spruce prefers moist, well-drained soil at low altitudes; it is often found mingled with red spruce and larch. Ordinarily a small tree, a specimen with a circumference of 7 feet and a height of 80 feet has been discovered at Vermilion Lake, Minnesota.

From a distance white spruce can be recognized by the silvery or bluish cast to its foliage, a color not found in any other native eastern evergreen. It is often mistaken for the blue spruce used as an ornamental. White spruce can withstand continued exposure to salt spray; solid groves descend to high tide mark along the rocky shores of northern New England.

The bark is a more ashy gray than that of the red spruce, but has the same scaly surface. The needles, a third to two-thirds of an inch in length, give off a skunk-like odor when bruised; in fact one local name of this tree is skunk spruce. The seed-producing cones, clustered among the higher branches near the top of the tree, bend downwards as they ripen to their maximum length of two inches. At first the cone scales are marked with a striking red border to the otherwise green scales, but later the whole cone becomes a glossy brown. The wood is used for paper pulp, having the same qualities as that of the red spruce.

Other Needle-leaved Conifers

BALSAM FIR is one of the most graceful and symmetrical of all the northern evergreen trees, its spires of rich green adding an ornamental touch to roadsides and open fields. Sometimes it is found in company with red and white spruces, birch and maple; but it also forms solid thickets which become the favorite winter retreat of deer. Visitors to New England may remember balsam fir best as the fragrant needles filling the "pine" pillows sold at roadside stands. Young campers remember it as the recommended tree from which to cut boughs for a woodsy mattress. Most city children of the East make an exciting first acquaintance with balsam fir as a Christmas tree, since it is the most popular evergreen for this use.

This fir is not a large tree, average individuals being thirty to forty feet in height. The largest fir balsam on record grows in Maryland; it has a circumference of 9 feet and a height of 75 feet. The straight trunk forms the axis for regular whorls of branches, each whorl smaller than the one just below it, until finally the last whorl of six or seven branches surrounds the tall recent-year's shoot. Unlike many evergreens the young trees can grow in dense shade. Thus hundreds of seedlings may often be found growing on the forest floor beneath other trees. Firs grow rapidly but are relatively short-lived, few trees attaining an age of over a hundred years.

The foliage of a balsam fir consists of flexible, flattened needles with blunt tips, arranged singly along the twigs. Each needle, about an inch in length, is a deep shiny green on the upper surface and a lighter gray-green beneath. The needles tend to be in two opposite rows and thus form a flattened spray; this is one means of distinguishing a balsam fir from a spruce. The dull brown bark is covered with thin scales and resin blisters, the blisters making this fir a sticky tree to handle.

In spring the many small pollen-producing cones form yellow clusters, while on the upper branches of the same tree erect female cones develop, ripening in fall into cylindrical purple-green structures several inches in length.

These seed-producing cones stand erect like plump colorful candles on the twigs.

Balsam fir wood is too soft and brittle to be useful as lumber. Its value, like that of the spruces, lies in its use as wood pulp. Its attractive appearance makes the balsam fir desirable as an ornamental, but it does well only in a moist cool climate and is very sensitive to smoke and fumes. For this reason it rarely thrives when transplanted to a city.

EASTERN HEMLOCK, also known as Canada hemlock, has flattened needles arranged along the twigs like those of the balsam fir. The needles are smaller, however —usually half an inch or less in length—and have lengthwise whitish lines on the undersurface. Even from a distance there is little chance of confusing the two trees, since the hemlock has an irregular open crown of foliage resulting in an airy and lacy appearance. Hemlocks are found where our forest trail leads through cool moist ravines, or beside mountain streams. They are slow-growing trees, not reaching full growth until two hundred and fifty years old, and even then having a life expectancy of an additional three hundred years! A large hemlock in Great Smoky Mountains National Park has a circumference of 17 feet, and trees 150 feet tall have been reported by lumbermen. Hemlock is the state tree of Pennsylvania.

Trunks of old specimens taper rapidly from a broad base and are protected by a ridged and scaly brown bark. This bark is the source of the tannic acid used in tanning leather. In earlier days trees were wastefully stripped of their bark and left to decay. Yellow, spherical, pollen-bearing cones appear in May, as do the equally small but green seed-producing cones. Mature cones are brown, and among the smallest of the evergreens, being only a half to three-quarters of an inch in length. The soft coarse-grained wood was originally disregarded for lumber, but with the decreasing supply of other available trees it is now being used for rough construction, crates, boxes and even paper pulp.

EASTERN LARCH, known in some localities as tamarack and hackmatack, is unusual in being a deciduous conifer. In autumn the foliage changes to a bright yellow, then the needles are shed, leaving the larch leafless in winter. In spring fresh needles give a delicate light-green tint to the entire tree, resembling the tender green of new deciduous foliage. In summer the larch can be recognized by its spire-shaped form and the more open and feathery foliage which sets it apart from the spruces and firs. Where our trail passes through swampy ground or skirts the low wet portions of fields, we will find larch growing in company with such other swamp-loving trees as spruces, alders, willows and red maples. Larches rarely reach great stature; the largest measured specimen with a circumference of 9 feet and a height of 90 feet is growing near Tamworth, New Hampshire.

The soft needles, about three-quarters of an inch in length, grow in rosettes of a dozen or more needles on short side stalks. No other eastern conifer has this habit. The reddish-brown bark of full-grown trees separates into numerous thin scales. The reproductive habits of this conifer are interesting because of the changes in the seed-producing cones, less than an inch in length. At first they are flattened spheres growing erect on the branches, colorful with their green and red bracts between the brown cone scales. After pollination the cones droop while the seeds are developing. Then they become erect again, opening their scales to release the winged seeds during fall and winter.

Larch wood is tough and coarse-grained, and therefore not generally desirable for lumber. Its durability, when in contact with soil, makes it especially suitable for railroad ties, poles, posts, and other such articles where exposure to dampness and earth would rot most woods.

The Scale-leaved Evergreens

Two trees of the northeastern states can be distinguished by their tiny scale-like leaves, which overlap to completely cover the twig on which they are growing. These are the arbor vitae and red cedar. They are both small trees with a dense cylindrical mass of foliage obscuring the main trunk and branches.

ARBOR VITAE (northern white cedar or swamp cedar) forms dense thickets along streams and cool swamps; it also grows in scattered groups throughout moist fields and pastures. When growing in the open arbor vitae is a picturesque tree, rarely more than forty feet tall, with a tapering and feathery tip. Many of the foliage-covered branches are flattened, presenting their narrow edges to view and producing a trim tailored appearance. An unusually old and large arbor vitae is growing in the ravine at Natural Bridge, Virginia; this tree has a girth of 15 feet and a height of 125 feet. Even in its wild state this conifer, more than most, resembles a cultivated ornamental evergreen.

The small scale-like leaves form flattened sprays which are dark green on the upper sides and a light yellowish-green beneath. When crushed the foliage gives off a spicy fragrance. Bark of old trees is fibrous, a warm orange-brown in color, and broken into fissures which often spiral upward around the trunk. The yellowish or reddish-brown cones rarely exceed a half-inch in length; they grow erect on the twigs, their few thin scales resembling the dried husk of a fruit.

Arbor vitae wood is too brittle and coarse-grained to be useful for construction purposes. However, it is used for posts, buckets, tanks, boats and canoe frames. It is also used in making shingles. The trim appearance of the tree makes it an attractive ornamental, and since it transplants easily is often used for foundation planting, windbreaks and hedges.

Scale-leaved Evergreens of the Northern Forest.

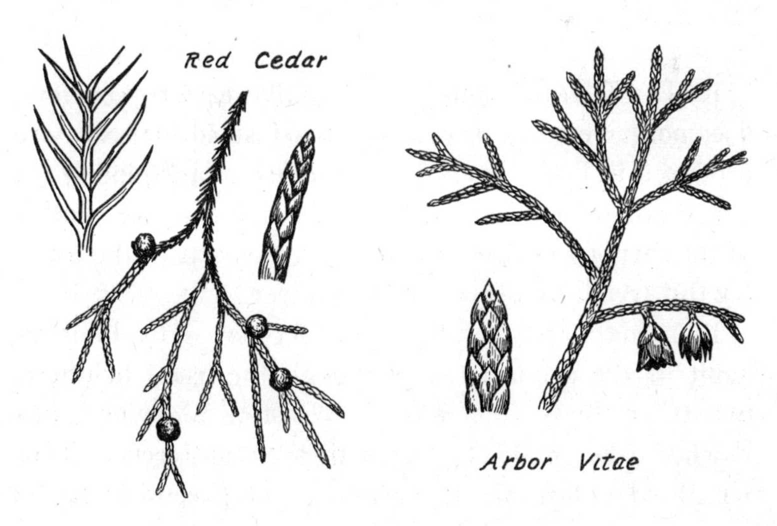

Red Cedars are familiar ornamentals as well as native roadside trees along the parkways of Connecticut.

RED CEDAR, unlike other native eastern conifers, does not have a dry brown cone but instead the seeds are produced in fleshy berry-like structures, dark blue and a quarter of an inch in diameter. Red cedar is a close relative of the shrubby juniper; in fact, in some parts of the country this tree is locally known as juniper.

Red cedars are small trees with the compact cylindrical habit of the arbor vitae. Although the usual height is twenty or thirty feet, a tree at Easton, Maryland, has reached a height of 54 feet with a circumference of 11 feet. Red cedars are the common evergreens scattered through old fields and pastures of New England, and are planted frequently along the parkways of Connecticut and New York. Young trees have sharply pointed awl-shaped needles, as do the young shoots of old trees. Older foliage consists of overlapping scale-like leaves which form a rounded or angular spray, thus differing from the arbor vitae with its pressed flattened twigs.

The reddish-brown bark shreds into narrow fibrous strips. The wood is well known for its pleasantly aromatic odor and pinkish color; it is commonly used in making cedar chests and closets, since the chemical nature of the wood provides a protection against insect attack. Red cedar wood is also a favorite in making lead pencils.

The Poplars

In those states where the living conditions are ideal for the development of the northern forest community, we also find a number of deciduous trees. Thus our trail may often lead through a mixture of the conifers we have just described, and a number of deciduous broad-leaved trees. In many places the entire woods may include only these trees. Most frequently encountered in northern United States are the various kinds of poplar, birch and maple. In addition we may discover willow, sycamore and elm.

This by no means includes all the deciduous trees we are likely to encounter along a forest trail in the northern forest. Others which occur are, however, better considered as members of the deciduous forest region.

QUAKING ASPEN, like all species of poplar, can be recognized by its alternate simple leaves and drooping tassel-like catkins. It is also known as the mountain aspen or golden aspen; it is a hardy cold-climate tree which spreads southward from Canada into the Rocky Mountain and Pacific Coast forests as well as into the Great Lakes states and New England. The name "quaking aspen" is appropriate because of the constant trembling of the leaves in the slightest breeze, caused by the flattened leaf stalks which permit the leaves to twist readily from side to side. Once you have seen the autumn-tinted hillside of the western mountains where aspen groves are displaying their bright yellow colors, you will appreciate the fitness of the name "golden aspen."

Quaking aspens often form groves and thickets on moist sandy and gravel soils. In the dappled shadows of their foliage the light yellow or green trunks add a pastel tint to the woods. The bark is smooth, but marked by horizontal creases and scars. It is the prized food of beavers, as is proved by the number of peeled and gnawed limbs and trunks around beaver dams. Buds and twigs are also eaten by deer, rabbits and ruffed grouse. Individual trees rarely reach a height exceeding fifty feet; their life span is short since they are easily injured by fire and attacked by fungus rot. The small rounded leaves have pointed tips and a finely-toothed margin, each leaf being from one to two inches in both breadth and length. Poplars are one of the few trees in which the male and female flowers occur on separate trees. The male catkins and the female catkins both appear on their respective trees before the foliage buds open. The wood of the quaking aspen is too soft and weak for construction use; it is however made

In the dappled light of forest glades, the light-colored bark of Quaking Aspens adds a pastel tint to the woods.

into matches, boxes and excelsior. It is also important as a pulp wood.

LARGE TOOTH ASPEN is also known as aspen, popple or just plain poplar. It is a larger tree than the quaking aspen, but like it spreads by means of root suckers to form dense thickets in abandoned fields and burned over woodlands. In comparison with the quaking aspen the bark is darker and more olive-green. The leaves, two to four inches in length, have irregular coarse teeth along their margins. Large tooth aspen is restricted to the eastern states, where its wood is used for the same purposes as that of quaking aspen.

EASTERN COTTONWOOD has a more spreading crown and broader habit than the aspens, being more elm-like in appearance. Also known as Carolina poplar and eastern poplar, this species is encountered wherever our

The Poplars: Flowers, Buds, and Foliage.

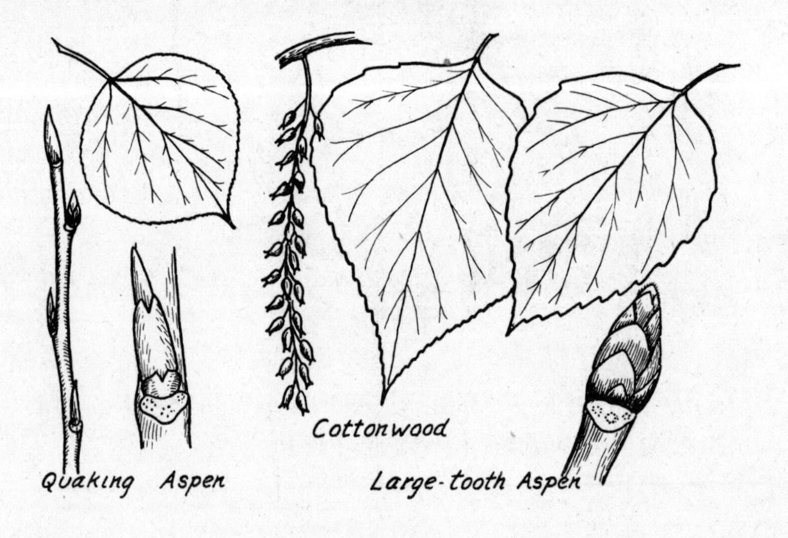

trail leads along open river valleys, flood plains and wet lowlands. Here cottonwoods are found in companionship with elms, willows and maples over a wide range from Maine to the Dakotas, south to Texas and Florida. Specimens over one hundred feet tall are found in favorable locations; a cottonwood at Fort Kearney, Nebraska, has a circumference of 30 feet. Cottonwoods become a welcome addition to treeless areas as well as to city streets because of the ease with which they adapt themselves to situations where other trees grow with difficulty. Yet they have several features which make them a nuisance. The mature catkins bear small fruits which split open to release millions of cottony-haired seeds which descend upon house and grounds in such quantities that their removal is a problem. Planting only male trees eliminates this situation. Another difficulty lies in the aggressive growth of the shallow but wide-spreading root system, which heaves up sidewalks and clogs water or sewer pipes. The rootlets have an uncanny ability to seek out the moisture and nutriment in these underground channels, bursting the pipes with their expanding growth. But to the grateful inhabitants of the prairie states of Kansas and South Dakota the shade of the cottonwood is particularly welcome. These two states have joined Wyoming in proclaiming the cottonwood their state tree.

The Birches

The birches are small to medium-sized trees which can be identified by their alternate simple leaves with distinctly toothed margins, and the presence of both male and female catkins on the same tree. Many of the species have a very distinctive bark, marked with conspicuous lenticels.

PAPER BIRCH, also called canoe birch and white birch, is one of the unforgettable trees of the northern forest. The chalky white bark and delicate foliage contrasts with the more sombre green of spruce and pine. Many northern lakes are fringed with paper birch, and many a highway in northern New England winds between rows of these stately trees. It is not surprising that the paper birch should be chosen as the state tree of New Hampshire, in whose forests it has made its home.

Full-grown trees have an open crown of foliage, with a few large limbs. They reach a height of seventy or eighty feet; a patriarch at East Northfield, Massachusetts, has attained a girth of 18 feet. The white bark peels easily in horizontal papery strips, revealing the pinkish or orange bark underneath. Being easily removed from the trees in large sheets, the bark was used by the Indians for making canoes, covering their wigwams, and fashioning household articles. Unfortunately this same peeling quality encourages thoughtless hikers and campers to pull off the bark for no particular reason. But to do this is likely to be fatal to the tree since it then permits fungus infection of the inner unprotected tissues.

Leaves of paper birch are oval, pointed and sharply-toothed; they vary from two to three inches in length. In spring the slender brown pollen-producing catkins hang downward in clusters. Farther back on the branches appear the greenish egg-producing catkins which ripen into brown cylindrical cones packed with tiny winged nutlets. The wood is tough, hard and close-grained; it is therefore used for turned articles such as spools and clothes pins. It is also used for wood pulp, and being long-burning makes both an attractive and effective fireplace wood. Paper birches have long been enjoyed as ornamental trees because of their unusual bark and pleasing appearance.

GRAY BIRCH is also appropriately known as poverty birch and oldfield birch due to its general appearance and choice of habitat. In some parts of the country it is called poplar birch because the small leaves flutter like those of the quaking aspen. It is the smallest of the birches, rarely exceeding thirty feet in height. Although its favorite haunts are along streams and in the moist soil of swamps, gray birch colonizes burned-over areas and abandoned pastures.

The Birches: Foliage, Catkins, and Buds.

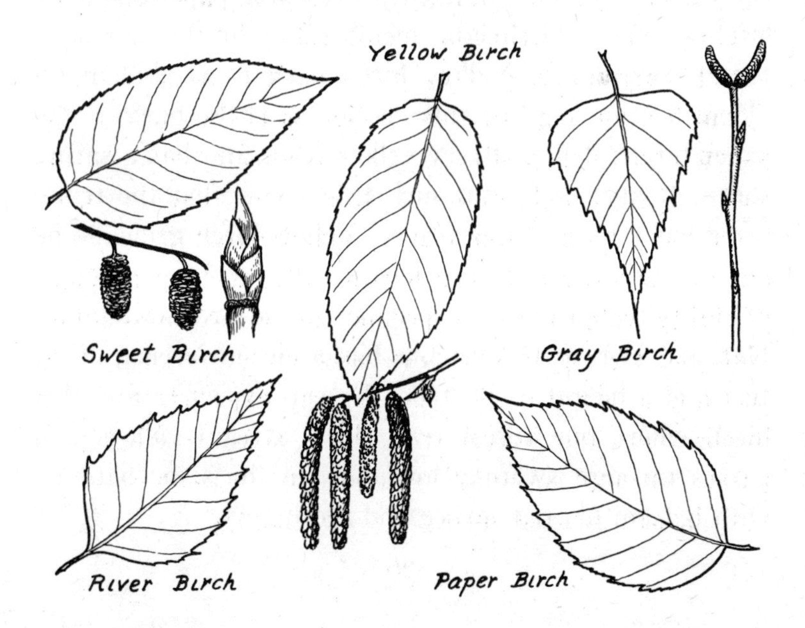

The closely branched slender main trunk supports a narrow crown of foliage; from a distance gray birches can be identified by their habit of leaning in various directions. The sloping and yielding trunks enable youngsters to take hold of the upper parts of the trees and use them as swings. The leaves are noticeably triangular, two to three inches long, with tapering tips. A shiny dark green on the upper side, each leaf is a much paler green on its underside. The bark of young trees is reddish-brown, somewhat like that of cherry trees; bark of older trees is a dirty gray, with no tendency to become chalky. The soft wood decays easily and has little commercial value except as firewood.

YELLOW BIRCH, known in some localities as silver birch or swamp birch, ranges southward from Canada into the Great Lakes states and northeastern United States. Thus this birch, like the preceding paper and gray birches, has a birthright membership in the northern forest community. Yellow birch bark is as evident an "identification tag" of this species as is the bark of the paper birch; it is a silvery yellow color and has a satiny sheen. It also peels into such thin strips that the trunk often has a ragged appearance. Yellow birch grows to be one of the largest eastern hardwoods, reaching a height of eighty feet or more. A specimen in the Green Mountain National Forest of Vermont has a circumference of 13 feet and a height of 88 feet. We can expect to find this birch where our forest trail skirts stream valleys and passes through swampy lowlands, in the same habitats with balsam fir, red spruce and red maple.

When growing in the open the trunk of a yellow birch is tall and straight, bearing a small rounded crown of foliage for the upper half of its length. The oval leaves, two to four inches in length, have sharply toothed margins and are a yellowish-green on the undersurface. The dull hairy twigs are an important difference when compared with the quite similar black birch. The hard close-grained wood is used in making furniture, flooring, interior finish and veneer. Deer, rabbits and beaver like to browse on the foliage.

SWEET BIRCH, also called black birch and cherry birch, is a member of the central deciduous forest which has made itself at home with more northern neighbors in the northeastern states. Sweet birch is found where our trail leads through thick forests and where the soil is rich in humus. The straight trunk often rises a considerable distance before branching, in a typical maple-like habit. Near Port Deposit, Maryland, a sweet birch has been found with a girth of 11 feet and a height of 80 feet. The species reaches its best development on the western slopes of the Appalachian Mountains.

As any boy brought up in the woods well knows, the name "sweet birch" refers to the fact that the bark has a delicious wintergreen flavor. Chewing the bark of young twigs is a woodsy substitute for candy. Commercial oil of wintergreen flavoring is secured from sweet birch bark. A drink known as birch beer is made from the sap secured from the trees in early spring. Numerous birds and mammals enjoy its buds, bark and seeds. Bark of young trees is a shiny reddish brown, marked with the usual lenticels.

On older trees the bark becomes black and furrowed into irregular plates. The oval leaves are very similar to those of the yellow birch, and the wood has the same qualities and uses.

RIVER BIRCH is a tree of river banks and swamps. Also known as red birch, it gains its greatest size in the bayous of the lower Mississippi Valley; river birch is frequently encountered, however, as far north as New York and New England. When growing in the open, river birch has a short stout trunk which soon divides into several main branches which grow upwards to form an open crown. The bark is a good "identification tag," being a cinnamon-brown color with a metallic luster, and peeling into papery strips. On old trees the bark separates into furrows and scales. River birch leaves are two to three inches in length, with wedge-shaped bases and pointed tips; the margin is distinctly toothed. Like the other birches, the wood is made into furniture and woodenware.

The Maples

Maples as a group can be identified by their leaf arrangement. The lateral buds, leaf-scars and leaves occur opposite each other and therefore grow in pairs. Poplars and birches have alternate leaves and leaf-scars. With the exception of the ash-leaved maple, all maples have simple leaves, divided into three- and five-pointed lobes. In spring the maples are abundantly covered with clusters of red or yellowish-green blossoms, often the first in the spring flower parade, before the leaves have appeared on the trees. In fruit the maples can be identified by their paired and winged "keys." In autumn they contribute the brilliant scarlet and gold foliage which creates the colorful landscapes at that time of year in New York and New England. There are thirteen species of maple in the United States; five of these occur in the northern forest.

SUGAR MAPLE goes by a variety of other names: rock maple, hard maple, black maple. It is native to every state east of the Mississippi River, being common either in pure stands or as scattered individuals in open woods and fields. A popular shade tree for streets and homes, it is so widely valued that five states have selected it to be their state tree: Vermont, Rhode Island, New York, West Virginia and Wisconsin. Sugar maple grows best on fertile well-drained soils but nevertheless is often found on rocky hillsides. In the open it produces a compact rounded crown of dense foliage. Sugar maples grow slowly but live

The Maples: Foliage, Buds, Flowers, and Fruits.

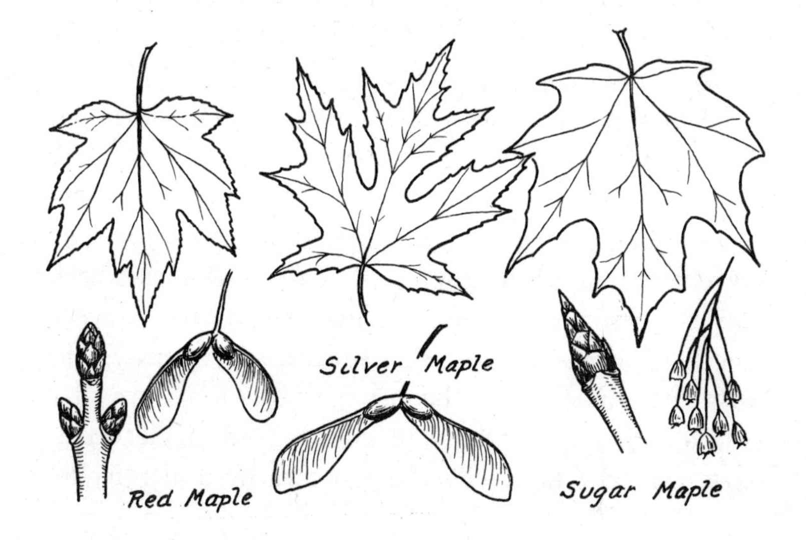

to be good-sized trees. A specimen at Bethany, West Virginia, has a circumference of 17 feet and is 110 feet high. The bark of young trees is smooth silvery gray, but becomes darker with age and furrowed deeply to form long narrow plates which are often loose along one edge. The leaves, three to five inches long, are five-lobed with a few teeth along the sides of the lobes. Male and female flowers are in separate clusters, but on the same tree; each flower is yellowish-green, with a five-lobed calyx and projecting stamens or pistil.

Groves of sugar maple, known as sugar bush, are tapped during late winter before the buds resume their growth in the northern New England and New York regions. Spigots are driven into the trunk and the sweet watery sap collected in buckets. Thirty gallons of this sap are needed to make, after hours of boiling, one gallon of pure maple syrup. Some of this syrup is further condensed to make maple sugar. The hard close-grained wood is of great value in making furniture, and for flooring and interior finish. It is outranked in hardwood lumber production only by oak and sweet gum.

RED MAPLE is also known as swamp maple because of its preference for wet lowlands and swamps; it is a member of the swamp community along every forest trail, from Maine to Florida. Red maple has a less dense crown of foliage than sugar maple, and a more slender tapering trunk with numerous smaller limbs which grow upwards. The bark of young trees is a smooth silvery gray, often mistaken for that of a beech; the same light gray bark is found on younger limbs of mature trees. Older bark is dark gray and flaky. The largest measured red maple is one at Susquehanna, Pennsylvania, which has a circumference of 15 feet and a height of 50 feet.

Red maple is one of the earliest flowering trees, its scarlet flower clusters appearing in March when most plant life still is deep in winter sleep, at the time when the first peeper choruses are echoing through the woods. In Florida the swamplands are red with maple blossoms in January, hardly giving the trees a chance to shed the red leaves of the preceding December. Not only are the blossoms red, but the twigs repeat the color, and the autumn foliage as well. The male flowers are sometimes found on one tree, and the female flowers on another. The winged fruits, also bright red when young, appear early in summer.

Red maple leaves, smaller than those of sugar maple, are three to five-lobed and sharply toothed along the margins of the lobes. The leaves can be recognized by the combination of a bright shiny green on the upper surface and a lighter silvery green on the underside. The wood has some of the features of sugar maple, and is used to a lesser degree in millwork and furniture manufacture; much of it is burned in kilns to make charcoal and wood acetate. The foliage and twigs are eaten by deer, rabbits, and beaver.

SILVER MAPLE, also known as soft maple and river maple, reaches its best growth in the Ohio River valley. It is usually a small or medium-sized tree, growing rapidly for the first fifty years of its life. However, a veteran silver maple at Harbor, Maine, has attained a circumference of 22 feet and a height of 90 feet. Its habit is very distinctive, the main trunk being short and soon branching out, elm-like, into a number of spreading branches which terminate in drooping branchlets with upturned tips. Silver maples can be expected where our trail leads along the moist soil of river bottoms and flooded valleys.

The leaves, with a maximum length of five inches, are deeply cut into five-pointed lobes, edged with deep notches between the teeth on each lobe. The silvery white of the underside of the leaf contrasts strikingly with the bright green of the upper surface. When disturbed by a breeze, the leaves turn about, showing their lower surfaces and thus giving a silvery sheen to the entire tree. The bark has a peculiar habit of flaking off in broad scales and strips, resulting in a ragged appearance. Silver maple wood is too brittle and soft to be of much value although it is used in cheap furniture and flooring, boxes and crates. It is also used for paper pulp, charcoal and wood acetate production. This species is planted quite commonly as an ornamental because of its tendency to "weeping" foliage and its rapid growth.

Some Other Deciduous Trees

Poplars, birches and maples include among their various species the most commonly encountered of the deciduous trees in the northern forest community. We will find many more along our trails in the northeastern and Great Lakes states, especially in the lowlands and along the southern margin of the area. At this time, however, we will take time to meet only the mountain ash, sycamore, American elm and black willow.

MOUNTAIN ASH is a small tree with a preference

for cool woods and secluded forest habitats. It is transplanted as an ornamental in the cooler portions of the northeastern states. Its brilliant orange-red fruit clusters make it a conspicuous and attractive tree during the late summer months. The feathery leaves are alternate and compound, consisting of eleven to seventeen leaflets arranged in pairs. Small white rose-shaped flowers appear in flat clusters in late spring, to be followed by the drooping clusters of berries. Although too acid to be used as a

Other Deciduous Trees of the Northern Forest.

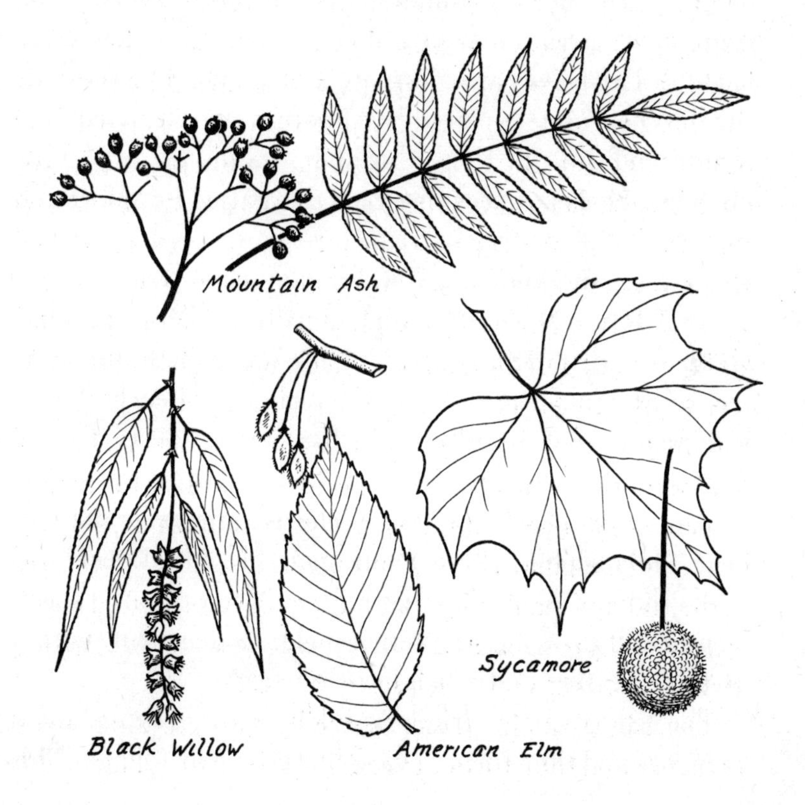

human food, the berries attract robins and ruffed grouse.

SYCAMORE is also known as buttonball tree because of its spherical fruit clusters which decorate the tree for most of the months that it is leafless. Sycamores are readily recognized by their bark, which forms a mottled pattern of brown, gray, yellow and white where different layers are exposed. The maple-like leaves are extremely large, reaching a length and breadth of eight inches. Sycamore twigs have an unusual zigzag habit; the buds are also peculiar in being conical, and protected by a single bud scale.

Sycamores often grow to massive proportions, reaching heights well over one hundred feet in their favorite surroundings: stream margins, flooded valleys and low river islands. The leaves are alternate and simple, like those of the birches and poplars. Sycamore wood is hard and tough, and difficult to saw or split; its unique use is for butchers' blocks. A cross between this native sycamore and the oriental plane tree is frequently grown as a street and shade tree, and known as the London plane tree.

AMERICAN ELM is undoubtedly the most familiar street tree of northeastern United States; it is the state tree of Massachusetts. Many famous trees of early American history have been elms. Such was the Liberty Tree in Boston under which the colonists met to protest the Stamp Act in 1765. The Penn Treaty elm is famous as the tree near Philadelphia where Penn made his initial overtures to the Indians inhabiting that region. A record-sized specimen is still growing at Wethersfield, Connecticut, with a girth of 30 feet and a height of 97 feet.

The short main trunk spreads into arching main branches and thus forms a vase-like crown of foliage. This

The main trunk of an American Elm spreads into arching branches which support a graceful vase-shaped crown of foliage, as in this New York state specimen.

typical shape is attained best in open fields; elms occur most frequently along river bottoms and in the fertile soil of wooded hillsides. The dark gray bark becomes furrowed with age into flaky ridges. Elm leaves are alternate and simple, with a saw-toothed margin and a peculiar lopsided base. In spring, before the foliage buds open, the branches are clothed with the clusters of purplish-green flowers, contributing their share to the awakening landscape. Elm wood is tough and cross-grained, and therefore difficult to work. It is used for sportsgoods, wheel hubs and in shipbuilding—wherever a tough hard wood is needed. Thousands of eastern elms are being threatened by the ravages of the Dutch elm disease, but this threat is being brought under control.

BLACK WILLOW is the most common of all the willows which grow to be good-sized trees. All the willows are catkin-bearing trees like the poplars and birches, widespread in colder climates. The black willow is a frequent member of the forest community along stream margins and in swamps. In fact, the term "willow" is generally associated in our minds with water. The alternate simple leaves are long and slender, up to six inches in length but rarely more than half an inch in width. The catkins appear in early spring, the male on one tree and the female on another tree. The appearance of these catkins is familiar to every boy or girl who has gathered pussy willows. Willow wood is of little value except for fuel and charcoal.

And now our trails through the northern forest have come to an end. We have not described every tree we might possibly find, so that the trees in this chapter do not make up a complete list of the native species of this forest community. If you have, in your own exploration of the woods of this region, found trees which do not seem to fit into the descriptions given in the preceding paragraphs, you will undoubtedly find many of them included in the trails we are going to explore in the deciduous forests of the central states.

Black Walnut fruits often remain on the branches several weeks after the leaves have fallen, as on this Maryland tree.

Chapter 5

TRAILS IN THE DECIDUOUS FOREST

IN THE central part of the United States is a region shaped like an inverted triangle which supports the largest deciduous forest in North America, extending as it does over a dozen states in the Mississippi and Ohio River valleys. The thousand-mile base of this triangle is its northern boundary, lying along the shore of the Great Lakes. In the Louisiana-Texas region a thousand miles to the south its apex touches the Gulf of Mexico. The eastern side of this wooded triangle is the backbone of the Appalachian Mountains, while the other side lies in the tier of states just west of the Mississippi River.

These fertile lowlands provide all the living conditions needed for growth of pure stands of deciduous trees. The land is for the most part low, level and fertile; when present, the hills are gentle and rolling. Much of the forest has disappeared in the wake of the westward movement of American pioneers, yet here and there we can find still many groves of original trees through which to wander on our forest trails. Some of the species have extended their range eastward and southward so that they are at home as well in the lowlands of New England and New York. Others have colonized the mountains and advanced to the Atlantic coastal plain to mingle with the trees of the southern forest community.

Some of the conifers of the northern forest have become members of the northeastern part of this deciduous forest. This is especially true in western Pennsylvania,

Ohio, northern Indiana and Illinois. Here we are likely to find such old friends as white pine, red pine, pitch pine and hemlock. In the swampy lowlands we can discover stands of larch, and in the open fields, scattered clumps of red cedar. The great majority of trees of the large central area of the country are broad-leaved and deciduous, however. In the cooler northeastern portion of this region, mingling with the northern conifers, grow the cool-climate deciduous trees of the northern forest—the birches and maples. Elsewhere the conspicuous trees are oaks and hickories; a great oak-hickory empire has developed in the Ohio valley.

The abundance and variety of deciduous trees which we encounter along forest trails in these central states may seem overpowering at first sight. We can lessen the confusion by taking three separate excursions into the woods. On one we will look only for those trees with *alternate and simple leaves*. This is the largest group and includes nine kinds of oaks as well as linden, sour gum, sassafras, dogwood, and tulip tree. On a second trailside exploration we will concentrate on those trees with *alternate and compound leaves,* a slightly smaller group which includes the locusts and hickories. The third trail will enlarge our acquaintance to the trees which have *opposite leaves,* some of which are simple (dogwood, catalpa) and others compound (ash and buckeye).

The Oaks

Just as the pines form a large, well-known group of evergreens, so are the oaks a most familiar deciduous group. Like the pines they occur in practically every state, and are as much a part of the landscape in Florida as in New England, in Ohio and Arkansas, as in California. Eight species of oaks are frequently encountered in the eastern states. All of these are deciduous; we shall discover later that some of the southern and western species of oak are evergreen. Most oaks are slow-growing, with resulting close-grained, hard wood. Tree rings in oak stumps indicate ages of five hundred years or more as being fairly common. Oak leaves are generally lobed or toothed, but a few species have entire margins. The leaves are always simple, and arranged alternately on the twigs.

Oak blossoms appear early in spring, at the time when the foliage buds are unfolding. The male flowers are minute, greenish-yellow and clustered in drooping catkins similar to those of the birches and poplars. The inconspicuous female flowers are produced at the bases of the leaf stalks and they develop into the familiar acorns. Each acorn is a fruit, consisting of a seed (the nut) enclosed in a scaly saucer or cup. Acorns are the favorite food of many birds and mammals: wild turkey, ruffed grouse, squirrel, chipmunk, deer and bear.

WHITE OAK is a valuable and attractive tree, its native home extending from southern Maine to Iowa, south to the Gulf states although it is rare near the ocean. White oak is found wherever our trail leads over rich, well-drained soil; it reaches its best development on the western slopes of the Appalachians and in the lower Ohio River valley. Many individuals are six feet in diameter and eighty feet in height. The patriarch of the white oak clan is the massive Wye Oak, growing at Wye Mills on the eastern shore of Maryland. This tree has a girth of 27 feet and a height of 95 feet. White oak is the state tree of both Connecticut and Maryland.

White oak has a sturdy main trunk with a wide-spreading and rounded crown of foliage. The pale gray bark, marked by scaly ridges, is a good identification tag, since few other oaks have similar bark. The leaves are edged by seven or more rounded finger-like lobes; white oak leaves change to a russet color in fall and remain on the limbs most of the winter. The egg-shaped nuts, three-quarters of an inch in length, are partly enclosed by the bowl-shaped cup. Very sweet in flavor, these nuts were boiled and eaten by the Indians, who also ground them into a flour for bread. With few natural enemies, this disease-resistant oak lives to a very old age. The strong, durable wood is ideal for furniture, floors and interior woodwork.

POST OAK, known also as box white oak and iron oak, grows on much poorer soil than the white oak; thus it can be expected on the same sandy and barren hillsides populated by pitch pine or red cedar. In these habitats it is ordinarily a small tree with stout gnarled branches and a low stature. In good soils, however, it grows to a greater size. A tree in Charlotte County, Virginia, has a circumference of 13 feet and a height of 80 feet. Post oaks are found from southern New England to Illinois and Missouri, south to the Gulf states; they are a common oak in central Texas.

The twigs can be identified by their covering of matted brown hair; the bark of old trunks is reddish-brown and marked by definite lengthwise ridges. Post oak leaves are thick, leathery and five-lobed; the two middle lobes opposite each other are the largest, giving a distinctive appearance to the leaf. The nuts of the acorns are a half-

The White Oaks of Eastern United States.

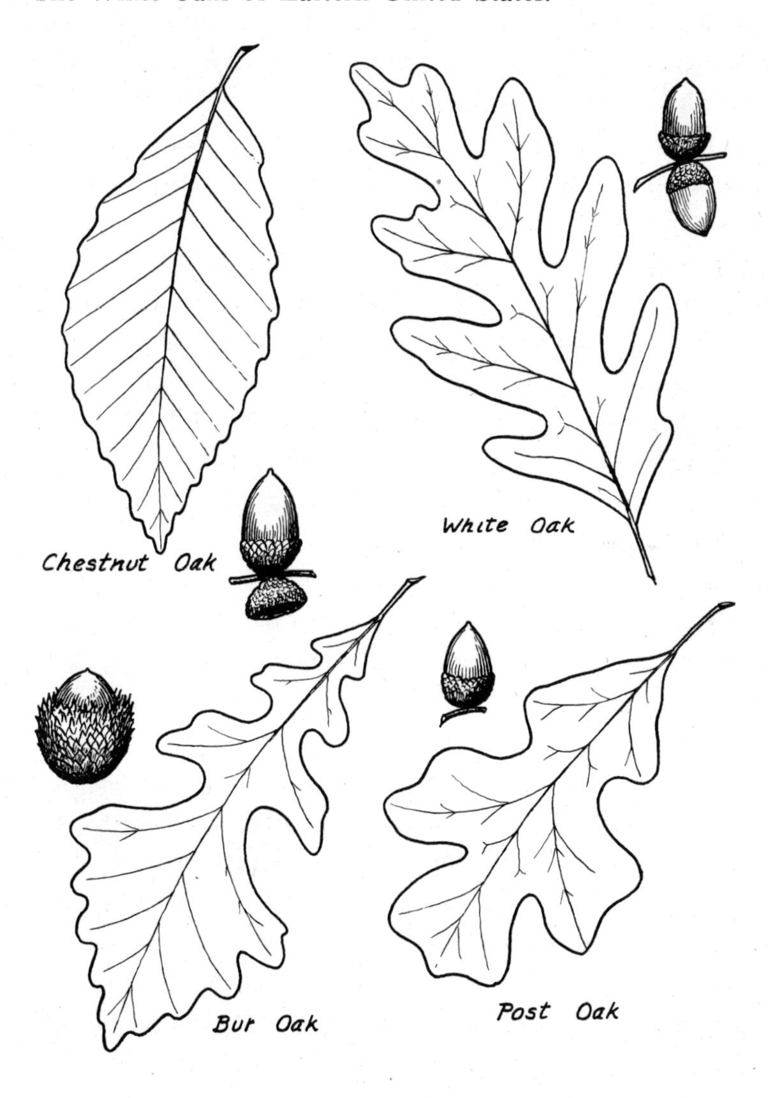

inch to two-thirds of an inch in length, buried in a deep cup.

BUR OAK, a large tree with the dimensions of a white oak, is easily recognized by the corky ridges on the smaller branches and by the large cup with fringed margin. For the latter reason, bur oak is also known as mossycup oak and overcup oak. This oak ranges from New England to the Dakotas and south to Tennessee and Arkansas. Bur oak is a familiar tree in Kansas and in the Wabash valley. The largest recorded specimen, with a circumference of 21 feet, is found at Charleston, Missouri.

The leaf of the bur oak is very large, some attaining a length of twelve inches! The rounded lobes are typical of this as of all white oaks, but in the bur oak two deep notches occur on each side. The underside of the leaf is downy and silvery green. On old trees the bark is grayish red and flaky. Bur oak wood is very durable when in contact with the soil, a usual feature of trees which grow in moist habitats.

CHESTNUT OAK is also known as rock oak or mountain oak because of its abundance on rocky ridges and exposed slopes. The name "chestnut oak" has been given it because the leaves resemble those of the chestnut in outline and in the coarsely-toothed margin; however, here the teeth are rounded, not spiny-tipped as in the chestnut. Chestnut oak has a more restricted range than most oaks, being found chiefly in the Appalachian Mountains from Pennsylvania to Tennessee and the Carolinas. It is usually a small or medium-sized tree about fifty feet in height; the main trunk divides not far from the ground into several large limbs, producing an open crown of foliage. A well-known patriarch is the Washington Oak near Fishkill, New York, under which General Washington is said to have regularly mounted his horse; it is 7 feet in diameter and is estimated to be eight hundred years old.

The bark of old trees is a good identification feature, being dark gray or black, and marked by distinct lengthwise ridges separated by deep furrows. The large leaves have a regularly scalloped margin with small rounded lobes. The meat of the oval nuts, enclosed in a deep bowl-shaped cup, is very sweet and edible. Chestnut oak wood, being heavy and strong, is used for the general purposes to which oak is put; the bark is of special value, being very rich in tannin.

RED OAK, a common tree of well-drained soils, is one of the most rapidly growing of all oaks. When living in the forest it has a tall straight trunk with a narrow crown. But planted in the open, the short stout trunk divides into several stocky branches to support a spreading mass of foliage which makes this oak a valued shade tree. A specimen at Loyd's Neck, Long Island, New York, has a girth of 18 feet and is 90 feet high. Red oak, which is the state tree of New Jersey, grows from Maine to Minnesota southward to the Carolinas and Tennessee.

The clean-cut leaves are recognized by their spiny-tipped lobes, of which there are seven to eleven. All of the preceding oaks have had leaves with rounded lobes. Their rich dark green color changes to a deep orange or red in fall. Unlike those of the white oaks, the acorns take two years to mature; this is also true of the following oaks. The nut, broadly oblong and about an inch in length, is borne in a flat saucer-shaped cup. Red-oak wood is widely used for flooring, for interior finish and for furniture.

PIN OAK gets its name from the numerous short stiff branchlets which grow on the lower limbs and which are very conspicuous when the tree is leafless. Pin oak is also known as swamp oak or water oak because it can grow

The Black Oaks of Eastern United States.

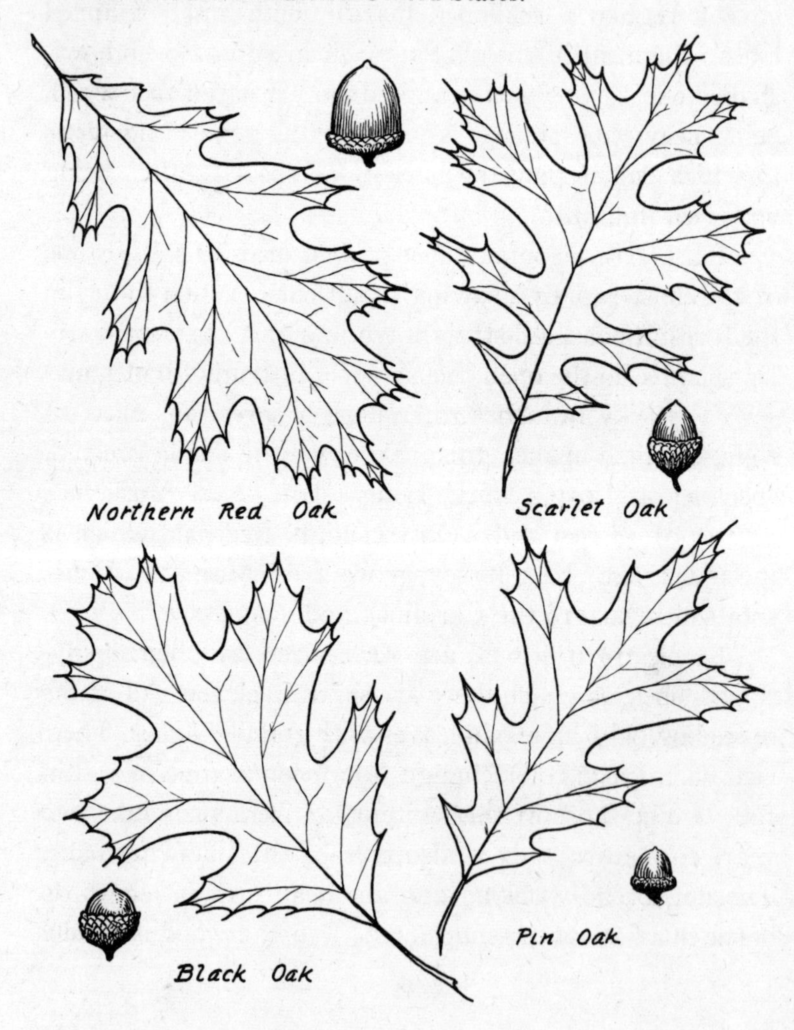

in poorly drained soils and wet lowlands. It is a favorite tree for street and park planting, partly because of its tolerance of city smoke and fumes, and partly because it is so highly resistant to attack by insects and fungi. Usually a small tree, a record specimen at Lawrenceville, New Jersey, has a circumference of 18 feet. Pin oak ranges from New England to Iowa, and as far south as Arkansas.

The bark of a full-grown tree is firm, gray or brown in color and covered with scaly ridges. Attractive lustrous green leaves are edged with five to nine lobes, each tipped with a sharp point and separated by deep indentations. The rounded nuts, less than half an inch in length, are set in broad shallow cups; wood ducks are especially fond of them. Pin oak wood has no special value as lumber because it warps and checks badly. Its chief use is for fuel, charcoal and distillation products.

SCARLET OAK is also known, unfortunately, as red oak, thus leading to some confusion. It is widely distributed throughout eastern United States. Rarely found in pure stands, it can be encountered along forest trails in a mixture with white pine and red oak, or with shortleaf pine and post oak. Its favorite habitat is light sandy or gravelly soils. A less massive tree than many of the oaks, it has slender branches and an open crown. A specimen at Forest Hill, Maryland, has a circumference of 11 feet and a height of 88 feet. Like the pin oak it is a rapid grower and thus is often used as an ornamental tree.

The sharply tipped lobes, seven to nine in number, divide the leaves almost to the midrib. Like many other oaks, the new spring foliage is bright red in color, but as the leaves mature they become a dark green, turning to bright red again in fall. The nuts, marked with thin light stripes, have a white kernel, in contrast to the yellow kernel of the black oak acorn.

BLACK OAK is one of the most familiar of the eastern oaks. It is also known as yellow oak and quercitron oak because of the orange-colored inner bark of the younger branches, from which the dye quercitron is made. Its home is the entire eastern half of the United States, although it is not abundant along the Canadian border or in the Atlantic Coast states. Old trees develop large upward-reaching branches which produce a wide-spreading crown of foliage. The main trunk is often massive, as is indicated by a tree at Millbrook, New York, which has a girth of 24 feet but is only 60 feet high. Black oak, usually a tree of well-drained uplands, grows also at times on poorer hillsides where other trees find it difficult to obtain sufficient water.

This particular oak has easily recognized bark, the ridges being split crosswise to form block-like sections; the bark is rich in tannin and is used as a source of this material. The wood is hard and strong; it is used in cheaper grades of furniture and flooring. Black oak leaves are much like those of scarlet oak, but the seven or nine spiny-tipped lobes are separated by indentations which extend only partly to the midrib. The large nuts are half-enclosed in the deep cup of the acorn.

Other Trees with Simple Alternate Leaves

Although the leaves or bark of the remaining deciduous trees in this group may be possible identification tags, the fruits are the most reliable guide. A spiny bur encloses the seeds of the beech and chestnut; a berry or similar fleshy fruit is produced by hackberry, mulberry, osage orange, cherry, sassafras, black gum and hawthorn; linden and tulip trees have wind-dispersed fruits.

BEECH is a tree with very distinctive bark; unfortunately it is sometimes scarred with initials and other reminders that human beings passed its way. The main trunk and all branches have a smooth, firm, steel-gray bark which on old trees is often spotted with darker patches. Beech trees occur in every state east of the Mississippi River except Florida. They become veteran members of the deciduous forest, and are common in rich woods and ravines of the northern forest as well; they often attain diameters of three and four feet, and a height of a hundred feet. Beeches thrive in deep fertile soil, often in company with birch and maple on open slopes or contrasting sharply with the dark foliage of hemlocks in damp ravines.

Beech and Chestnut: Foliage and Fruit.

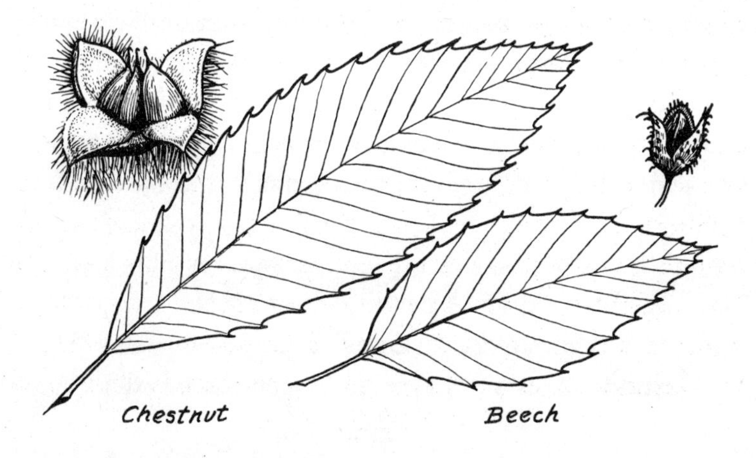

Beech leaves have a papery texture; the veins extend in parallel rows from the midrib to the margin of the leaf, each vein ending in a sharp tooth. Male and female flowers are borne on the same tree, the yellowish-green male flowers hanging in rounded clusters and the small female flowers grouped in pairs, covered by protective bracts. The female flower develops into a soft-spined bur containing two or three triangular nuts. Beechnuts have a sweet flavor, and are a favorite food of deer, bear, raccoon, squirrel and various game birds.

The spreading and shallow root system gives rise to new trees as root sprouts. Thus old beeches are generally surrounded by a thicket of their offspring. Full-grown trees are inviting in their shade, since the long horizontal limbs support a low and spreading crown of foliage. Beech wood is hard and heavy, but difficult to split. The clean odor and light color make it suitable for barrels and boxes in which food is packed; it is also used for furniture and woodenware.

CHESTNUT is a close relative of the beech, but has had the misfortune of near-extinction by the chestnut blight, a disease brought unknowingly into this country from Asia in 1904. As a result the species which was once the delight of every schoolboy from Maine to the southern Appalachians has now become a memory. Eastern forests are still filled with standing dead chestnuts, bleached reminders that trees too have their severe epidemics. No adequate method of control has yet been established, nor has a blight-resistant American chestnut been discovered. Sprouts and young trees can often be found, however.

Chestnut leaves are larger and more pointed than beech

leaves, but otherwise resemble them, especially in their coarsely-toothed margins. The male flowers are produced in long slender catkins; the smaller clusters of female flowers produce large spiny burs which split open when ripe to reveal several oval nuts, flat on one side. Chestnuts have a sweet nutritious meat, greatly enjoyed before the trees became so rare by hikers through our northeastern forests.

HACKBERRY, or sugarberry, is a medium-sized tree easily confused with an elm. The main trunk produces a few large branches which support a wide-spreading but rounded crown. Hackberries can be identified when in fruit by the dark purple berries, much like cherries, but smaller and with a sweeter taste. Remaining on the tree during the winter, these provide a generous supply of food for birds. A hackberry tree 14 feet in circumference and 85 feet high is growing at Pemberville, Ohio. Hackberries are favorite shade trees in the prairie states, although as ornamentals they often present a ragged and unkempt appearance.

Leaves of hackberries are oval, with pointed tips and margins which are regularly toothed except at the base of the leaf. The bark of old trees is very distinctive, because of numerous wartlike projections; otherwise the bark is a smooth silvery or brownish gray. Clusters of male and female flowers, each an inconspicuous yellowish-green, occur both on the same tree.

RED MULBERRY is a small tree with stout and often crooked branches; it is usually found where our trail takes us across rich bottomlands, in a mixture with other deciduous trees, throughout the eastern states. The oval leaves are heart-shaped, or occasionally two- or three-lobed, with toothed margins; their stalks exude a milky sap when cut. The edible fruits resemble large blackberries and are eaten

Some Eastern Trees with Alternate Leaves.

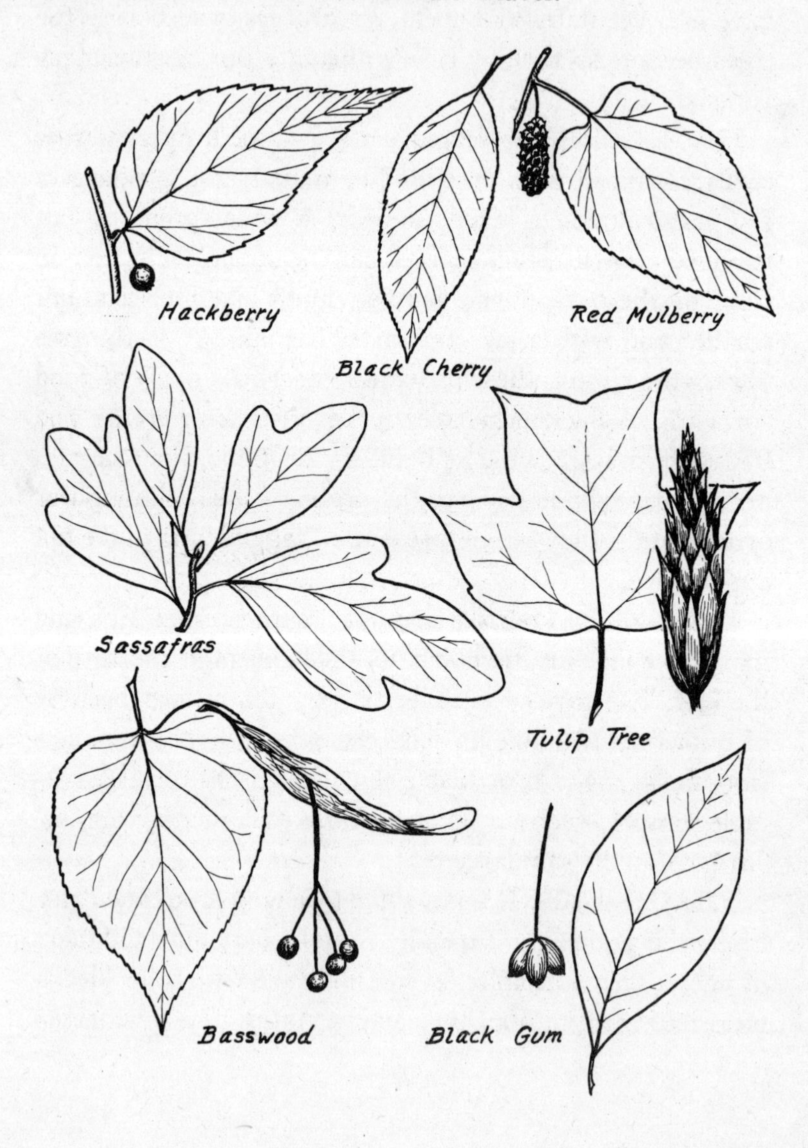

by robins, catbirds, and thrushes. Housewives often pick whatever berries the birds have left, to make into pies and jellies.

OSAGE ORANGE is an interesting tree, originally found only in its native home of the Arkansas and Red River valleys in south central United States. However osage orange has been found to be well able to withstand drought and has become a tree of many uses. A hardy tree, it has been introduced throughout eastern United States as a hedge tree and windbreak. Isolated individuals are often found throughout the eastern woods as far east as Maryland and north to the Great Lakes. It is a small thorny tree whose branches form a tangled mass, ideal for a "living fence."

Osage orange leaves are oval and glossy green, with smooth margins. The bark is unusual in having orange-colored fissures between the ridges; this yellow wood was used as a dye by the Indians. Small greenish male and female flowers appear in June on separate trees; the female flowers develop into green knobby fruits the size of a small orange. Osage "oranges" have a not-unpleasing spicy odor but a flavor which is distasteful even to hungry animals. Osage-orange wood is strong and flexible, much in demand during the horse-and-buggy era for making hubs and spokes of wheels. It is still highly prized by archers as wood for the manufacture of bows.

BLACK CHERRY has a variety of other names, among them rum cherry, wild cherry and cabinet cherry. It is one of several kinds of cherries growing in eastern United States, and found in both the northern and the central forests. Full-grown trees bear twisted horizontal branches, supporting an open crown of foliage. When in blossom, the cherries are familiar even to amateur naturalists. They grow on a variety of surroundings, but are frequently encountered on dry upland soils where many more fussy trees will not grow. Old trees reach a diameter of several feet and heights of a hundred feet.

Young trees can be recognized by the satiny reddish-brown bark, marked by horizontal lenticels. The bark of older trees breaks into irregular plates which are easily separated from the tree. It is easy to confuse a black cherry and a black birch when the trees are leafless; a simple test is to taste the bark of young twigs. Cherry has a bitter, puckery flavor, the birch a sweet wintergreen taste. Leaves of black cherry are a shiny green, lance-shaped and edged with fine teeth. In spring, after the leaf buds have opened, clusters of the five-petalled white flowers appear. This contrasts with the cultivated cherry, whose blossoms appear before the leaves. In summer the flowers become drooping clusters of dark reddish-black fruits the size of peas. Although bitter, these cherries appeal to ruffed grouse, bear, raccoon, porcupine, skunk, and fox; the pits are eaten by mice and chipmunks. Cherry wood is well known for its attractive reddish color and close grain; it has been prized for many years in making furniture and for interior trim. The tree is unsatisfactory as an ornamental because of the numerous diseases and pests which attack it, especially the tent caterpillar.

HAWTHORNS form a confusing group of trees, consisting of at least a hundred different species. A beginner would find it difficult to identify any particular kind of hawthorn. They are low, spreading trees with closely tangled branches, armed with long sharp thorns. When leafless they are easily recognized by the unbranched thorns; these protect the trees from grazing animals, so that hawthorns grow unmolested in fields and pastures. The trees are very adaptable for growing in any surrounding, serving as excellent erosion control vegetation.

The small leaves, oval or wedge-shaped, are edged with teeth. When in blossom hawthorns can readily be mistaken for small pear or apple trees because of their white or pinkish flowers, each with five spreading petals. The scarlet fleshy fruits resemble rose hips or small apples, the hard bony seeds being embedded in a flesh which is either tasteless or very tart. Squirrels eat the seeds, discarding the fleshy portions of the fruit.

SASSAFRAS is a small or medium-sized tree of the eastern states, occurring from southern New England to Iowa, south to the Gulf states. It can grow on sandy and poor soil, and for this reason is often found along fences and roadsides. A shrub in the northern part of its range, sassafras becomes a small tree in the woods of Maryland and Pennsylvania, and reaches a stature of forty or fifty feet in the Great Smoky Mountains. Sassafras is easy to identify by the greenish color of young branches and twigs whose bark has a pleasant and spicy taste. Open-grown trees have stout branches which reach upwards to form a flat-topped crown.

Sassafras leaves are confusing because they vary in shape, even on the same tree. Some are wedge-shaped without any lobes, others may have one large and one small lobe so that the leaf looks like a mitten, still others may be three-lobed. Our colonial fathers thought sassafras bark had great medicinal value; sassafras tea was once considered a "must" among spring tonics. Oil of sassafras and an orange dye are made from the bark and wood. Sassafras foliage contributes colorful reds and yellows to the autumn landscape. The greenish flowers occur in small clusters which can be easily overlooked; the male and female flowers develop on different trees. The fruits, on the other hand, are excellent identification features, being dark blue berries borne on bright red stalks.

BLACK GUM—also known as sour gum, tupelo and pepperidge—is found wherever our trail takes us over bottomlands and moist slopes. It is usually a small and compact tree, forty feet or less in height. Its range is from southern New England west to Illinois and south to Texas. An unusually large specimen with a girth of 18 feet and a height of 109 feet is growing at White Hill, Maryland.

The best recognition tag is the blue-black fruit which resembles a miniature plum; even though oily and acid, the fruit attracts game birds and some mammals. The small oval leaves turn a brilliant and shiny red in autumn. Black gum wood is tough, and hard to split, but it is used for gunstocks, broom handles, rolling pins and similar articles. It is also used as a core on which to glue other more valuable woods as a veneer. Both male and female flowers are inconspicuous and greenish-yellow and are found on the same tree.

BASSWOOD is also known as American linden, lime tree, bee tree and whitewood. It is an impressive tree with a compact narrow crown, the largest trees being found in fertile valleys near streams. A basswood at Queenstown, Maryland, has a circumference of 14 feet and is 75 feet high. This species is fairly common from Maine to Minnesota, but becomes of less frequent occurrence south of Tennessee and Arkansas.

The large heart-shaped leaves with sharply toothed margins are quite distinctive. Bark of old trees is dark gray and checked by horizontal cracks in the ridges. In early summer the branches bear clusters of fragrant, creamy-white flowers which attract bees with a resulting production of basswood honey. The nut-like fruits, each the size of a small pea, are clustered beneath a leafy bract which acts as a parachute when the seeds are ready for dispersal. Basswood makes a good shade tree because of its habit and rapid growth. Old basswoods often have hollow bases which provide nesting accommodations for small mammals and birds.

TULIP TREE, or whitewood, is a stately tree with a tall straight trunk and a narrow crown of foliage. It is also known as tulip poplar or yellow poplar, names which are misleading since it is not a true poplar. Another common name, tulip magnolia, is more appropriate since it does belong to the magnolia family. Tulip trees are common where our trail leads through rich woods in the portion of the eastern states with mild winters, from southern New England to Illinois and south to the Tennessee-South Carolina highlands. Forest-grown trees often have a clean trunk for a hundred feet before the first branch begins. An old tulip tree at Annapolis, Maryland, has a girth of 26 feet. There is good reason why four states—Indiana, Kentucky, North Carolina, and Tennessee—have selected this handsome species as their state tree.

The bark of young tulip trees is a good identifying

Tulip Tree blossoms are large and distinctive, consisting of three green sepals and three yellow petals marked with orange.

feature; it is a smooth gray, marked by lighter-colored lengthwise streaks. Older trees have firm and evenly-ridged bark. The best recognition feature is the unique leaf. Square in outline, the leaf is broadly four-lobed; the tip is depressed and notched at its center, and two gracefully pointed lobes form the base of the leaf. The large tulip-like flowers, several inches in diameter, are very distinctive but unfortunately they usually occur only on the upper branches and are out of reach for identification. Each flower bears three large green sepals and three yellow petals marked with orange at their base. The grayish-brown cone-like fruit-clusters, resembling those of the magnolia, remain erect on the branches and persist through the winter as an additional identification tag.

Tulip tree wood is soft and easily worked, and thus is used for interior finish and as a core for veneers. The flowers are sought out by bees for making honey.

The Nut Trees

In addition to the familiar fact that these trees bear various kinds of edible nuts, they can be recognized by their large compound leaves, alternately arranged on the stem. Except for the leaflet at the tip, all are arranged opposite each other in pairs along the central stalk. Most of the nut trees are as common in the northeastern states as in the central and southern ones. The group is described here, however, because hickories are most abundant in the central deciduous forest.

BLACK WALNUT, also known as American walnut or eastern walnut, is native to the entire eastern region. It is relatively rare, however, in northern New England and New York, and is found only infrequently along the Atlantic coastal plain. Black walnut usually grows among other deciduous trees on the deep rich soil of river bottoms. Old trees six feet in diameter and over one hundred feet high were once very common, but are now rare because of excessive cutting for lumber. A specimen in Anne Arundel county of Maryland has a girth of 19 feet and is 100 feet in height. From a distance black walnut is readily identified by the airy effect of its feathery foliage.

Each compound leaf consists of at least fifteen, and sometimes as many as twenty-three lance-shaped leaflets; the terminal leaflet is no larger than the others. The male flowers are clustered in drooping catkins; the smaller female flowers grouped in two's and three's at the tips of the twigs. Both kinds of flowers are produced on the same tree. The large spherical green fruits, several inches in diameter, are present on the branches for several weeks after the leaves have fallen. Since the husk does not split open, the nuts are released only by the decay of the fleshy covering, which turns black as the husks lie on the ground during the winter. The sweet edible meat is as highly prized by many mammals as by man.

Black walnut is one of the most valuable of all American hardwoods. The close-grained, rich brown wood is used for fine furniture, cabinetmaking, veneers and gunstocks. Walnut trees germinate readily and can be transplanted easily; they therefore are often used for ornamental purposes. An added feature in their favor is the open crown of thin foliage which allows sufficient light to reach the ground for growth of grass beneath the trees.

BUTTERNUT or white walnut has a more restricted range, growing from Maine to Minnesota but occurring rarely south of Tennessee and Arkansas. It prefers moist soil, and thus is most commonly encountered where forest trails lead near streams. Butternut is usually a spreading tree with a short main trunk; a specimen at Grover, Wisconsin, has a circumference of 9 feet and a height of 110 feet.

Butternut leaves consist of leaflets much like those of the black walnut, but these rarely exceed fifteen in number, and may be as few as eleven. The best identification tag is the flattened terminal bud, a half inch in length, which is very different from the shorter and rounded terminal bud of the black walnut. Pollen-producing flowers

The Nut Trees: Foliage and Fruit.

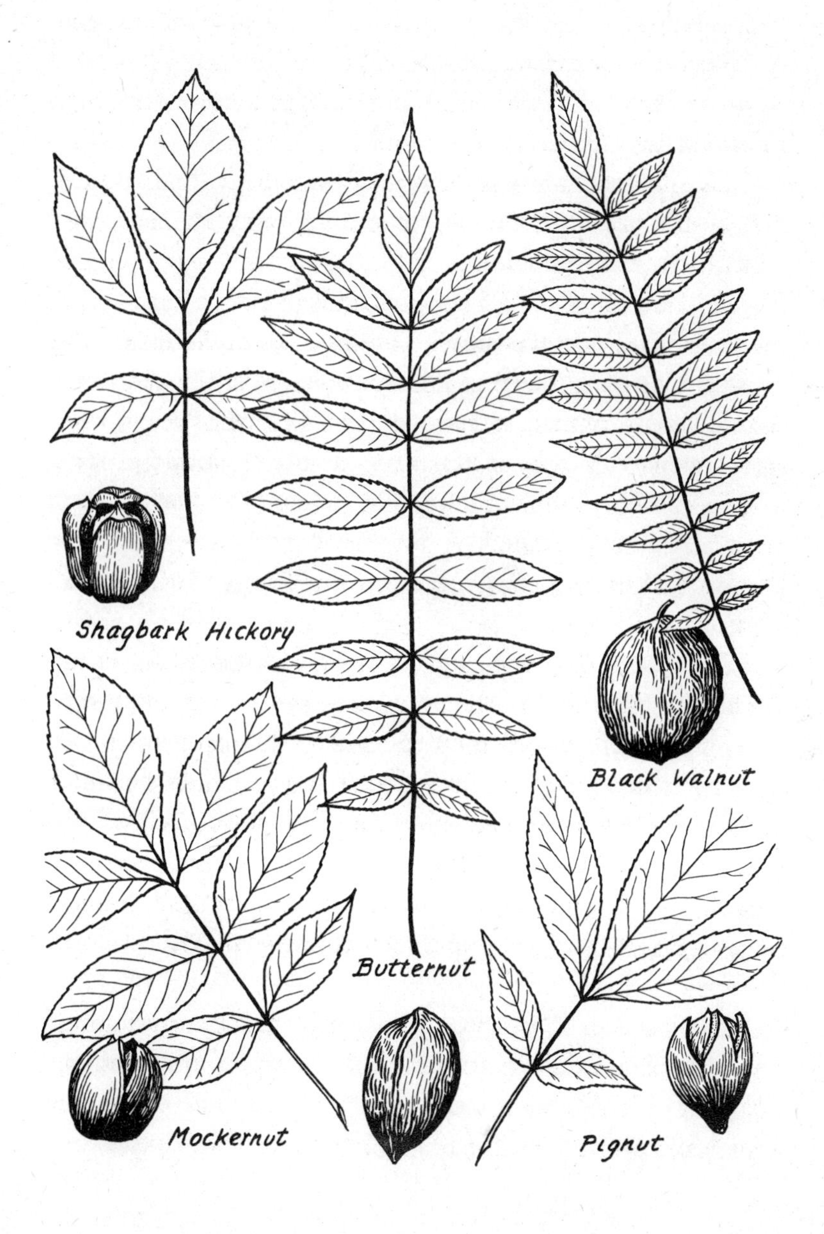

are borne in the usual catkins, and the female flowers in small groups at the tips of the branches. Butternuts are enclosed in gummy pear-shaped husks, several inches long. As the name suggests, the kernel is rich and oily. The soft weak wood is of little value in construction or furniture manufacture.

PECAN trees are commercially the most valuable of the native nut trees. Growing originally only in the south central states from Illinois and Missouri to Louisiana and Texas, they have now been introduced into a number of southern and eastern states for their valuable crop. The trees can be recognized in late summer or fall by the four-parted husks which remain on the branches after they have opened to release the nuts. Pecans are large trees with spreading limbs and an open crown; the bark is dark gray and firmly ridged. A patriarch tree in Assumption Parish, Louisiana, is 21 feet in circumference and 135 feet high.

Each pecan leaf consists of fewer leaflets than either the black walnut or butternut; there are usually only nine or eleven narrow and pointed leaflets. Long slender catkins form drooping clusters of male flowers, and the small female flowers are grouped at the tips of the twigs. The thin-shelled pecan nuts have a high food value. Much of the crop still comes from wild trees, although planted pecan groves are becoming increasingly abundant from Georgia to Louisiana.

BITTERNUT, or swamp hickory, can be found along forest trails bordering streams and swamps from southern Maine to Minnesota and far south to the Gulf states. Its best recognition feature is the bright yellow, dotted terminal bud. The leaves, smaller than any of the preceding nut trees, consist of seven to eleven narrowly-pointed leaflets; the terminal leaflet is larger than the others. An exceptionally large bitternut is growing in West Feliciana Parish, Louisiana, with a circumference of 12 feet and a height of 171 feet. Husks of the bitternut fruit split into four parts, revealing a rounded nut with a thin shell. The meat is so bitter that the nuts are ignored even by squirrels. The light, weak wood is used to some extent for flooring, furniture, boxes and crates; its greatest value is its use for fuel, and for smoking hams and bacon.

SHAGBARK HICKORY, also known as scaly-bark hickory and upland hickory, is an easy tree to identify when full-grown because of the gray bark which splits lengthwise to form long loose plates, attached at one end or at the middle. This hickory is likely to be found where our trail crosses open hillsides and climbs rocky slopes; its range is from southern New England to Iowa, but is rare along the Atlantic Coast. Although lumbermen have reported specimens a hundred feet in height, the largest measured tree is at Avon, Connecticut, with a girth of 10 feet and a height of 68 feet.

The leaves ordinarily consist of only five leaflets, each wedge-shaped and narrowing toward the base. The large oval terminal bud is surrounded by spreading dark-brown scales. Shagbark hickory fruit has a thick husk which splits into four sections, releasing the small white nut with edible kernel. Like other hickories, the wood is well known for its combination of strength, toughness and elasticity. It is used for wheels, athletic equipment, handles of tools and as a fuel for smoking meats. Both wild and cultivated varieties provide the hickory nuts found in the markets.

MOCKERNUT is also called white-heart hickory and big bud hickory. Growing in a variety of habitats from rich river bottoms to rocky ridges, it ranges from southern New England to Illinois, southward to the Gulf states. The name "mockernut" is well deserved, for the large plump husk contains a disappointingly small nut; the kernel, however, is sweet and edible. Full-grown trees have a stout central trunk with the lower branches dipping towards the ground. Not as large as some of the hickories, an unusually old tree at Loch Raven, Maryland, is 11 feet in circumference and 86 feet high.

Mockernut leaves usually consist of seven rounded and toothed leaflets, but may be either five or nine in number. The male flowers are clustered in catkins at the base of the new growth of leaves; the female flowers, in two's and three's, develop into brown fruits an inch in length. The husk splits into four parts to release the rounded nut. Mockernut wood is similar to that of the shagbark hickory and is used for the same purposes.

PIGNUT HICKORY shows a preference for dry and well-drained ridges and slopes; it is common from southern New England to Illinois, south to Alabama. A narrow, compact crown of foliage is supported by branches which are often twisted and contorted. In the southern Appalachians trees five feet in diameter and a hundred feet high have been reported by foresters. One recognition feature of this hickory lies in the smoothness of the stalks and lower surfaces of the leaves, which consist of five to seven leaflets. The husk of the fruit is pear-shaped, containing a thin-walled nut with a bitter kernel.

Shagbark Hickory in winter displays the tracery of limbs which becomes revealed, as in all deciduous trees, after the leaves have fallen.

The Locusts

Locusts have compound leaves arranged alternately on the twigs, like those of the nut trees. They are decidedly different, however, in having thorny or spiny branches and trunks. So few of the trees which we meet along forest trails have thorns that this characteristic alone makes recognition easy. We have already met two trees with this identification tag: the hawthorns and the osage orange. Both of these have simple leaves. Locusts are the only trees of common occurrence in the eastern states which combine thorns with compound leaves. An additional recognition feature, if one is needed, is the fruit—a pod similar to that of a pea or bean. This is not remarkable when we realize that locusts are members of the pea family.

HONEY LOCUST is also known as sweet locust, thorn tree and three-thorned acacia. We are likely to encounter isolated specimens where the trail skirts lake shores and stream margins. The feathery foliage consists of compound leaves divided into numerous small oval leaflets, an inch or less in length. In some cases the leaflets are again subdivided into smaller leaflets, resulting in what botanists call a twice-compound leaf. The branches and main trunk are armed with stiff branching spines, several inches in length. Honey locust ranges from New York and Pennsylvania to Iowa, and southward to Texas, reaching its best development in Indiana and Illinois. It is relatively rare east of the Appalachians.

Honey locust blossoms are small and an inconspicuous green, with the male and female flowers occurring on the same tree. The fruit is a large purplish-brown pod, flattened and twisted into a spiral shape. The pulp of the pod has a sweet taste (hence the name "honey" locust) and is eaten by cattle, deer, rabbits and squirrels. The drooping clusters of flowers are fragrant and much sought after by bees as a source of nectar for their honey. Honey locust wood is hard and durable, most useful as posts and railroad ties. Old trees reach a circumference of twelve feet and heights of eighty feet or more. They are frequently used for shade trees, and as shelterbelt plantings in the Midwest.

The Locusts: Foliage, Flowers and Fruit.

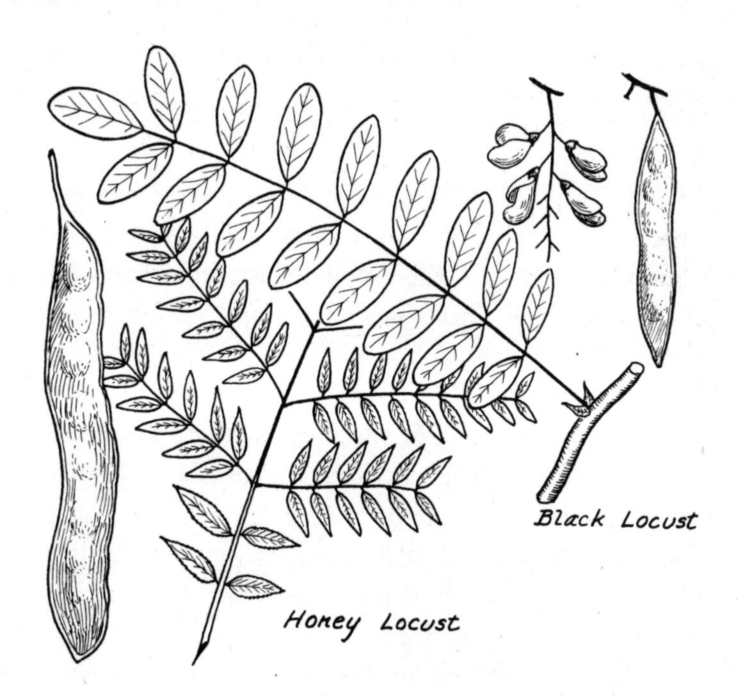

Black Locust can be recognized when in blossom by the showy drooping clusters of pea-shaped flowers.

BLACK LOCUST—also known as yellow locust, common locust and false acacia—is a medium-sized tree whose original home was in the Appalachian and Ozark Mountains. It has been introduced into many other states, so that now it is found as far north as Maine. Black locust grows frequently along streams and in moist well-drained soil, but also colonizes borders of woods and abandoned agricultural land. Locusts form thickets readily because of their habit of producing young trees by root sprouts. The roots, like those of alfalfa and clover, restore nitrogen to the soil. Thus black locust is used for reclamation and restoration of soil fertility.

The coarsely-ridged trunk bears a few scraggly branches

which support an open crown of foliage. Long compound leaves consist of seven or nine oval leaflets, light yellowish-green in color. The branches bear pairs of stout thorns at the base of the leaf stalks; they are unbranched and much smaller than those of the honey locust. Drooping clusters of showy white flowers adorn the tree in spring, very similar to wisteria blossoms. The fruit is a small flattened and straight pod, tan or light grayish-brown in color; it remains on the leafless branches during the winter. Black locust wood is also used for fence posts and railroad ties. Although it has many qualities desired in an ornamental, its use is limited because of its numerous insect pests.

Trees with Opposite Leaves

As we try to identify the trees along our forest trails, we can consider ourselves fortunate when we find one whose leaves, buds and branches occur in pairs or three's. Such an opposite arrangement indicates that the tree is either a flowering dogwood, catalpa, buckeye or ash. None of these is likely to be confused with another.

EASTERN DOGWOOD is easily recognized during every season of the year. In winter the upward-curving tips of the slender branches remind us of the antlers of a deer; the swollen flower buds at the tips of the twigs are an unusual turnip-shape, and the bark of full-grown trees has an alligator-skin appearance. In spring, usually before the foliage develops, the showy dogwood blossoms appear. Each blossom is several inches in diameter, with four large white or pink bracts, notched at the tip; these surround a central small cluster of yellow flowers. In summer the simple oval leaves are readily remembered because the large primary veins curve to follow the margin of the leaf. In autumn the leaves change to a warm purplish-red; long after the leaves have fallen to the ground the bright red dogwood berries adorn the branches. It is surprising that only Virginia has selected this attractive species as its state tree.

Dogwood trees are generally under forty feet in height, with a short irregular trunk and spreading branches; they form an under-story beneath the taller maples and oaks, as well as groves in open fields. Dogwoods thrive in rich well-drained soils from southern New England to Iowa, south to the Gulf states. The wood is ideal for shuttles in weaving, pulleys, golf club heads and mallets. It is a widely planted street tree from Connecticut to Florida.

WESTERN CATALPA, or Indian bean, is also known to children as the cigar tree because of the long slender cigar-shaped fruits. A tree of moderate proportions, abundant in rich bottomlands from Indiana and Illinois southwards to Arkansas, this catalpa has been introduced as a street tree as far north as Massachusetts. Catalpa has several unique recognition tags. The large heart-shaped simple leaves grow in two's and three's on the branches. The blossoms are very showy, occurring in large erect clusters; each individual flower is white, spotted with purple, and the petals are fused to form a small upper lip and a large lower one. The fruits, bean-like capsules a foot or more in length, hang on the branches all winter; they contain many small winged seeds. A record-sized tree growing at Ellicott City, Maryland, has a girth of 17 feet

In spring, before the foliage develops fully, Dogwood trees are covered with a dazzling array of snow-white blossoms, well illustrated by this grove in Indiana.

and is 58 feet high. Catalpa wood withstands decay in damp soil, and thus is used for fence posts and railroad ties. Another species, very similar in all its features, is a native of the Atlantic coastal plain.

Some Eastern Trees with Opposite Leaves.

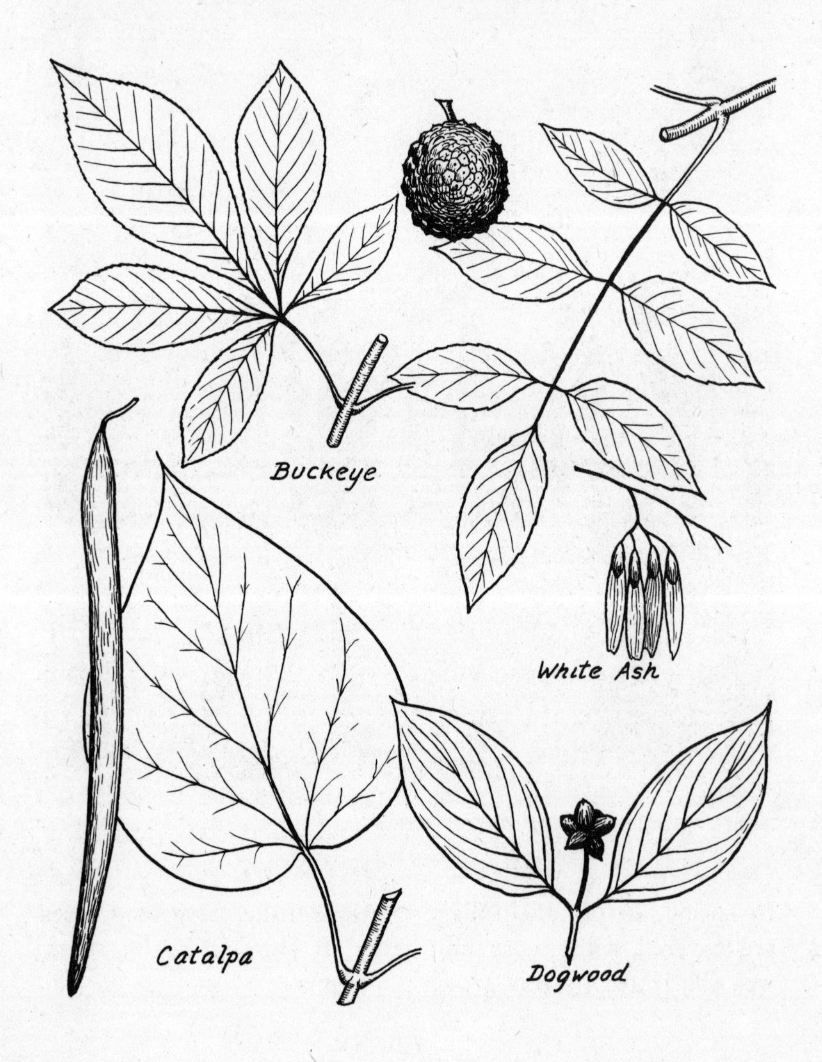

BUCKEYE, more accurately known as Ohio buckeye since there are other species in the Appalachians and the western states, is a relative of the horse chestnut, and is common from Pennsylvania to Iowa, south to Arkansas. It is the only native tree with opposite compound leaves whose leaflets radiate out from the center of the leaf stalk like the spread fingers of one's hand. Each of the five leaflets is broadly lance-shaped, tapering to a point. From a distance, buckeye can be recognized by its short main trunk which divides to form stout drooping branches. It is usually a shrubby tree, although a specimen at Elyria, Ohio, has a circumference of 8 feet and is 90 feet high. This tree is so common along the Ohio River that Ohio has long been known as the Buckeye State; it is natural that this species should be the state tree.

The ashy gray bark is broken into large scaly plates. Another identification mark is the large brown terminal bud. After the leaves have appeared, stiff clusters of yellowish-white flowers develop, less spectacular than those of the introduced horse chestnut. Later in the season the prickly fruits appear, an inch in diameter and containing a single brown shiny nut. This nut is inedible, and is believed by some to be poisonous to cattle. The wood is used for boxes and crates; more recently it has been found ideal for artificial limbs.

BLACK ASH. The ashes are all opposite-leaved trees with stout twigs and large broad terminal buds. Each leaf is compound, consisting of leaflets arranged opposite each other in two rows similar to the arrangement in walnut and butternut. Small flowers, lacking petals, develop in clusters before the leaves appear, the male and female flowers usually being on separate trees. The wind-dispersed fruits have a single wing, resembling the blade of an oar. Black ash is also known as hoop ash and basket ash because the coarse-grained wood separates into layers which can be woven and bent. The large compound leaves usually consist of seven or nine leaflets without stalks; each lance-shaped leaflet has a pointed tip and a toothed margin. Black ash is partial to wet woods, swamps and river banks. Its range is from New England to Iowa, south to Virginia.

WHITE ASH is another common species, differing from the black ash in having the leaflets stalked. It is the largest of the ashes; a tree at Glens Mills, Pennsylvania, has a circumference of 19 feet. White ash leaves generally consist of seven leaflets, oval and with a smooth margin. The long straight trunk has gray bark distinctively sculptured into diamond-shaped fissures and interlacing ridges. White ash has a more extended range than black ash, occurring from New England to Minnesota and south to the Gulf of Mexico. It is a valuable timber tree because of its elastic and tough qualities; it is particularly desirable for agricultural implements, athletic equipment and tool handles.

This brings to a close our trailside explorations in the great deciduous forest of the central states. As was evident when the ranges of the trees were described, most of the inhabitants of this forest community also live in the northeastern states where trees of the northern forest have their home. When we make the acquaintance of the trees in the southern states, we will find there, too, many of the species described in this chapter. However, it is in the great expanse of the central plains east of the Mississippi River that the deciduous trees introduced in this chapter have reached their greatest development. Thus we have met them on their home grounds.

There have been many omissions, which may make it difficult for you to identify trees near your home or along your city streets. The omissions include those trees which have been introduced from other parts of the United States or from foreign countries. Some of these have escaped into the woods and fields and may be found mingling with the native species.

Chapter 6

ROADSIDE TRAILS IN THE EAST

MANY NATIVE MEMBERS of the two types of forest communities we have just described in the preceding chapters are planted as ornamentals. Some are selected for their general attractive appearance, others because they are excellent as windbreaks or for shade. All must have one quality in common: an ability to withstand city smoke and fumes, and to survive in soil conditions less favorable than are present in the woods.

Among the native conifers planted for ornamental purposes in the northeastern states are hemlock, white pine, red pine, red spruce, larch and arbor vitae. The deciduous trees used for this purpose include American elm, sugar maple, silver maple, sycamore, cottonwood, paper birch, catalpa, dogwood, tulip tree and various oaks. In addition to these our streets and highways are landscaped with a number of immigrants from foreign forests. Pines and spruces have been introduced from Europe. The maidenhair tree, an unusual relative of the pine, has been brought from China. Such European and Asiatic trees as Norway maple, horse chestnut and ailanthus have become more familiar to some city dwellers than the native maples and oaks.

Some Introduced Pines

AUSTRIAN PINE is a sombre-hued evergreen whose scaly trunk is grayish-black, but whose smaller branches are a warm reddish-brown. This pine can easily be confused with the native red pine, since both have the same general appearance and both have two long needles to a cluster. The needles of the Austrian pine are stout and stiff, however, in contrast to the softer and more flexible needles of the red pine.

Austrian pine is a native of Europe and western Asia, introduced into the United States a century ago. Although considered a good timber tree in its native Austria, it has coarse and knotty wood in the United States, where it is grown mainly as an ornamental. The cones, slightly larger than those of the red pine, have prickly tips to the scales. Austrian pines grow in any kind of soil, and survive even the rugged winters of Maine. The stiff, sturdy branches can stand high winds and heavy snows; thus the trees make good windbreaks.

Introduced Eastern Evergreen Trees.

SCOTCH PINE is more scraggly and of a dwarfed appearance, looking much like a pitch pine. Observation of the foliage reveals the difference; Scotch pine has two short twisted needles to a cluster, whereas pitch pine has three. In its native Europe, Scotch pine often grows to be a tall and impressive tree with wood of commercial value. It makes up a large portion of the forests of northern Germany and Russia. A reliable identification feature, noticed even at a distance, is the orange-red bark of the younger branches. Scotch pine is a hardy pioneer, thriving in all kinds of soils from Maine to Nebraska.

Other Introduced Conifers

NORWAY SPRUCE, a common species in Europe, is a favorite ornamental evergreen not only in the northeastern states but in the north central states as well; it is found as far west as North Dakota. Like all spruces it grows best in a cool humid climate. Its dark green spire of foliage consists of whorls of drooping branches, the lowermost often touching the ground and smaller branchlets hanging down from the main limbs. This gives a weeping effect to the tree, making it the easiest evergreen to identify from a distance. Norway spruce grows well on almost any soil, but reaches its greatest height and age (about eighty feet and one hundred years) on well-drained soils. Many a New England farmhouse is protected from the wind by a shield of Norway spruces, and in the prairie states they form effective windbreaks along edges of fields and around farm buildings.

The bark of Norway spruce is usually well hidden by

Norway Spruce is a favorite ornamental conifer in cool, humid portions of the United States.

the foliage; on older trees it is reddish-brown and scaly. The four-angled needles, slightly less than an inch in length, point upward and completely clothe the twigs. The clustered pollen-producing cones resemble plump yellow catkins; the larger seed-producing cones are comparatively fewer in number. These cones, at first a greenish-purple, change to brown when mature and hang downwards from the boughs.

Two other common conifers, the blue spruce and the Douglas fir, have been introduced from the Rocky Mountain forests. These will be described in greater detail in later chapters. They can be mentioned in passing, however, since they are likely to be included among ornamental plantings in the eastern states.

The Maidenhair Tree

MAIDENHAIR TREE, or Ginkgo, is a most unusual tree for several reasons. Known as the "living fossil" of the tree world, it occurs today only as a cultivated tree even in its native home in China and Japan. Before the last glacial period it was widely distributed, and the fossil Ginkgo leaves look almost exactly like those of the living trees. Another unique feature is the thin fan-shaped leaf which resembles those of the maidenhair fern, even though Ginkgo is actually a close relative of the conifers. This species was introduced into England in 1750, and from there came to the United States twenty years later. In this country maidenhair tree is a familiar street and park tree in cities as far north as New York and Springfield, Massachusetts.

A straight tapering trunk supports a spire-like crown of foliage. The fan-shaped leaves have no midrib, and are deeply notched at their rounded tip; in fall the leaves turn a clear yellow before they fall to the ground. When leafless, numerous short stubby branchlets can be seen, arising at right angles from the main limbs. Inconspicuous flowers appear in early summer, the small male catkins and the paired female flowers on separate trees. The fruits are yellow, fleshy and similar to cherries. When they fall to the ground the fleshy pulp decays and emits an offensive odor. Thus male trees are preferable for ornamental planting. Inside the flesh is a silvery white nut, prized by Orientals and used as a special treat at banquets.

Introduced Eastern Deciduous Trees.

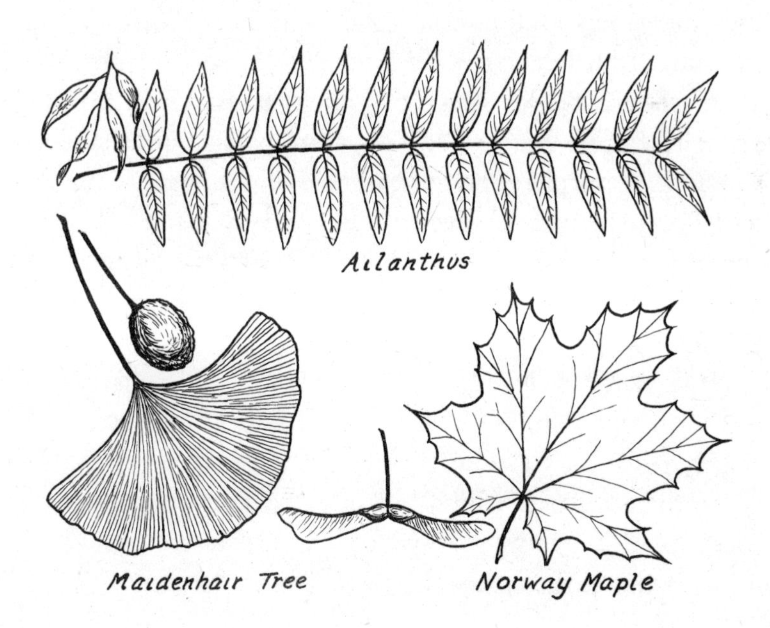

Some Cultivated Broad-leaved Trees

HORSE CHESTNUT, a native of southern Asia, was introduced from Europe in the eighteenth century and has since become a familiar American tree. Some horse chestnuts are still standing in Fredericksburg, Virginia, which were planted by George Washington. The name "horse chestnut" may come from the fact that the nuts were a legendary cure for sick horses, or because the leaf scars are the shape of a horse's hoof.

The arching limbs support a broad spreading crown, thus furnishing excellent shade; the lower branches tend to droop and then turn upwards at their tips. The bark is a dull gray or brown broken into broad scales separated by shallow fissures. Horse chestnut leaves are oppositely arranged on the twigs, and are easily remembered since they are compound, consisting of leaflets radiating as in the native buckeye. Unlike buckeye, horse chestnut has large showy flower clusters which stand erect on the branches. Each flower has five white petals, spotted with yellow and purple. The corky husk of the fruit, covered with blunt spines, is several inches in diameter. Within are two or three shiny reddish-brown nuts, too bitter to be edible. Horse chestnut wood is used for boxes, veneers and artificial limbs.

NORWAY MAPLE has opposite simple leaves, as do most of the maples; these are usually five-lobed and closely resemble those of the sugar maple. Norway maple is a European tree which has adapted itself well to city conditions. It grows rapidly, has an attractive crown of foliage, and is free from diseases. The difference between

Horse Chestnut is an attractive tree when in blossom, with its showy erect clusters of white flowers.

a Norway maple and a sugar maple on the basis of foliage is evident when we break a leaf stalk; that of the Norway maple secretes a milky juice, which the sugar maple does not.

Bark of mature tree is firmly ridged, with narrow fissures. This too is different from the sugar maple, whose bark is furrowed into long thin plates. Norway maple blossoms appear in late spring, covering the branches with yellowish-green clusters before the leaf buds open. The paired wings of the fruits are set at a wide angle, at times almost in a straight line. The leaves contribute a sunny yellow to the autumn colors of New England.

AILANTHUS, or Tree-of-Heaven, is a rank growing shrubby tree which has brought pleasure to thousands of city children who perhaps otherwise would never see a tree close at hand. Clumsy branches form an open flat-topped crown, and the gray bark develops fissures which are light in color and crisscross between the low ridges. The extremely long, compound leaves offset the unattractive appearance of the branches by their tropical and palm-like aspect. No other tree has made itself so thoroughly at home in poor soil, amid the soot and grime of cities, as ailanthus. It thrives on ash heaps, littered backyards and in narrow strips of earth between paved alleys. Ailanthus was brought to the United States from its native home in China, and in a few decades has become a forest weed in many localities.

Each compound leaf, often two feet in length, bears thirteen to thirty-five narrow leaflets and could be confused with the foliage of tree-size sumacs. However, the leaf scars of ailanthus are large and shield-shaped, rather than small and U-shaped. The sap of sumac is milky, while that of ailanthus is not. Many small greenish flowers are borne in clusters, male on one tree and female on another. The male blossoms give off an offensive smell so that female trees are preferred for ornamental planting. The reddish-green fruits occur in large clusters, each fruit being a central seed surrounded by a double-pointed papery wing.

LOMBARDY POPLAR has a narrow cylindrical crown which has made the tree popular in formal gardens, and for borders of driveways and lanes. It was introduced from Europe in the colonial days. Although not long-lived, some specimens reach a height of a hundred feet. The alternate simple leaves are triangular in shape, with a pointed tip and a wedge-shaped or rounded base. The smaller twigs and branches are yellowish-brown, and tend to grow upwards as a sheath around the main trunk. Bark on old trees is gray and deeply furrowed.

WEEPING WILLOW, a native of China, was also brought to this country in early colonial days. It is ordinarily not a large tree, a height of fifty feet being considerable for a weeping willow. It is hardly necessary to say that this species is a favorite for planting around streams and pools in parks and on estates. The rounded crown sweeps downward in hundreds of long slender drooping branches which hang from the larger limbs. Weeping willow leaves are narrow and pointed, alternately arranged on the twigs. All willow trees can be easily propagated from branch cuttings.

Bald Cypress trees, such as these on the swampy borders of the St. Johns River in Florida, are usually draped with Spanish moss. Their peculiar "knees" can be seen at the lower left.

Chapter 7

TRAILS IN THE SOUTHERN FOREST

EAST of the Appalachian highlands, on the gentle piedmont slopes and on the flatter coastal plain, is a well-defined forest which contains many trees not found elsewhere in the United States. To anyone accustomed to the evergreen and deciduous forests of New England and the north central states, the difference is striking, increasing in fascination as our forest trails extend southward. This is a vast evergreen forest in which species of pine are the conspicuous members. In the low and swampy portions of the forest, along the seacoast and up the river valleys, the dominant tree is the picturesque cypress. A tropical aspect to the forest is contributed by the palms, also trees of moist lowlands. Bordering the open glades and pond margins grow majestic live oaks and evergreen magnolias.

Most of this forest grows in a humid, warm region which is tropical as it reaches the tip of Florida. The mild climate encourages the growth of epiphytes—plants which live on other plants, without need for contact with the ground. One such epiphyte is Spanish moss, whose gray-green festoons hang from the branches of pine and oak alike. Dense mats of ferns cover the horizontal limbs of the live oaks and the rough leaf-bases of the cabbage palm. Air plants which resemble small pineapples perch on the sides of cypress and maple. All this creates a forest wonderland which it is difficult to adequately describe.

We can consider that the southern forest has its beginnings in Maryland and Virginia. As our forest exploration moves southward we find the first southern yellow pines, live oaks, cypress, holly and magnolia. At this northern edge of the forest we can find also many of the trees encountered in previous chapters. White pine occurs on higher ground as far south as Georgia; pitch pine and eastern hemlock likewise occur in the Appalachians as far south as the Carolinas. A few familiar trees—white oak, American elm, dogwood, red maple—appear both in the woods and in roadside plantings as far south as Florida.

Our special interest, however, lies in those trees which are restricted more or less to the southern forest, rarely growing north of the Mason and Dixon Line or crossing the Appalachians to the north central states. These include the southern pines, bald cypress, some deciduous and evergreen oaks, several broad-leaved evergreens such as magnolia and holly, palms and mangrove.

The Pines

There are few forest trails we can explore in the southeastern states without meeting one or more of the southern pines. They may form solid stands in park-like groves, miles in extent; or they may mingle with each other and with the broad-leaved trees in a mixed forest community. The pines have slender needle-like leaves in clusters of two or more needles; being conifers, they also can be recognized by their woody cones in which the wind-dispersed seeds are produced. Two of the southern pines—longleaf and loblolly—have *three needles* in a cluster. Three species have *two needles* in a cluster; these are slash, shortleaf, and Virginia pines.

The Southern Pines.

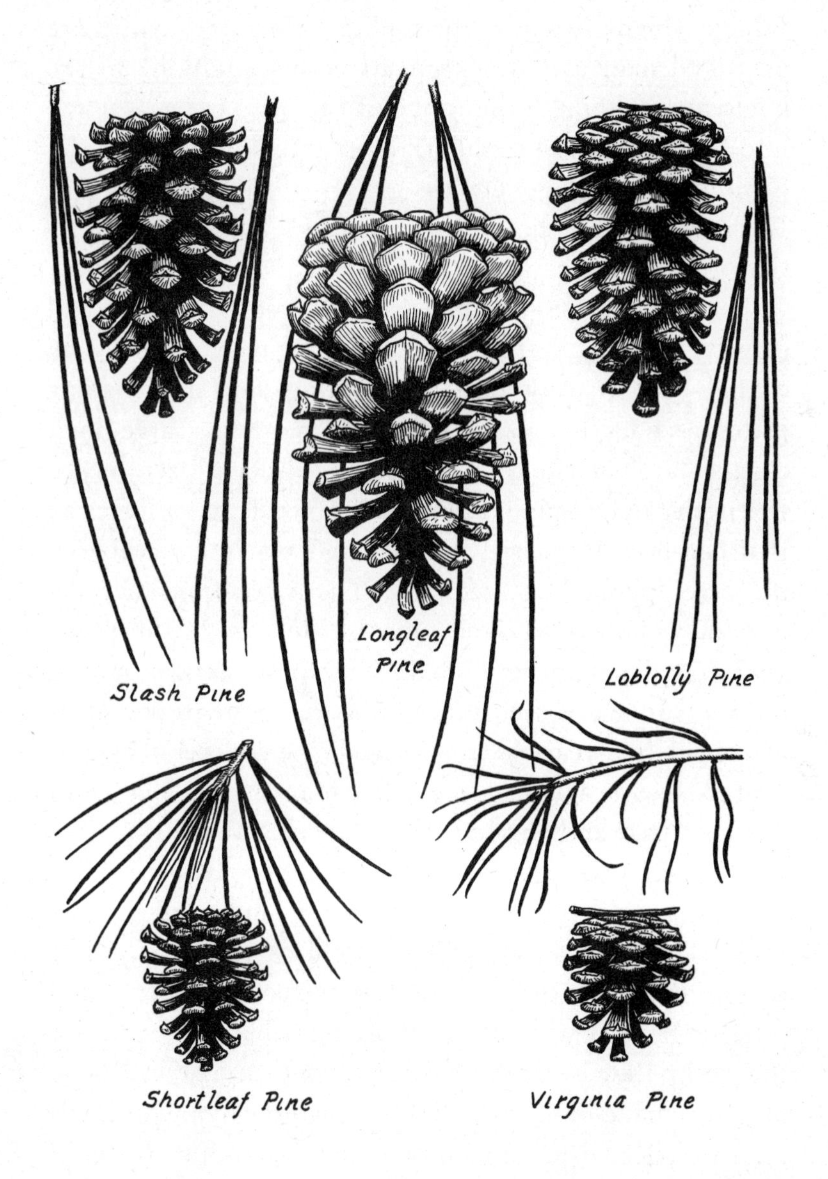

LONGLEAF PINE is a handsome tree with tall straight trunk, topped by a bushy crown of rich green foliage which glistens in the sunlight. Few trees which are useful to man are also such attractive additions to the landscape. Although the range of this pine extends north into Virginia, it is a common forest tree only south of the Carolinas. Seemingly endless groves of this pine occur in Florida and line the highways of the "deep South" of Georgia and Alabama.

The trunk of longleaf pine, several feet in diameter and often a hundred feet in height, can be recognized by its orange-brown scaly bark, separating into rectangular plates. As its name suggests, the needles (three in a cluster) are very long; sometimes needles eighteen inches in length can be found. Each flexible needle has a luster as if it had been lacquered; this is particularly noticeable in the erect plume-like seedlings. These seedlings develop best in well-drained sandy loams; during the first two years they remain very small while developing a strong tap root. In succeeding years, however, growth is unusually rapid, five-year old trees often being six feet in height. Mature seed-bearing cones are five to ten inches long, with flattened base and a rounded and tapering shape.

Longleaf pine was formerly the most valuable tree of the southern forest; it is used both for lumber and for its resin. The hard strong wood is sold as southern yellow pine, suitable for general building purposes, flooring and interior trim. The trees are more valuable, however, for the resin they secrete. A slash about twelve inches in length is made in the bark, from which the dripping crude gum is collected in a metal or pottery container fastened beneath the slash. Year after year new cuts are made in the bark, to tap a fresh surface of the trunk. The crude gum is distilled to form turpentine and rosin, known as naval stores; they are used in paint and varnish manufacture, soap making, manufacture of paper and production of insecticides. Naval stores have long been the basis of an important forest industry of the South; longleaf pine is one of the leading producers on which the industry relies for the crude gum.

LOBLOLLY PINE has this unusual name because it grows in moist depressions known in the South as "loblollies." It is also called oldfield pine because of its ability to colonize old agricultural land. Like the longleaf pine it is a tree of the coastal plain, from Maryland to the Gulf states and west to Texas. The tall cinnamon-brown trunk supports an open crown of pale green foliage. Its maximum size is indicated by the measurements of an odd loblolly pine near Carmichael, Maryland, which is 16 feet in circumference and 84 feet high.

The deeply furrowed bark of a mature tree, divided into oblong plates, is thick enough to protect the tree from the numerous fires which are constantly burning in the southern pine forests. The needles, in clusters of three, are usually less than eight inches in length and thus are shorter than those of the longleaf pine. As additional identification of this tree, the needles are stiff and twisted. The seed-bearing cones, smaller than those of the longleaf pine, mature the second year; the cone scales are tipped with stout spines. Loblolly pine is valued as a timber tree because of its hard wood and its rapid rate of growth; a tree can grow to a height of seventy-five feet in thirty

Slash Pine, like Longleaf Pine, is tapped for its crude gum which is distilled into turpentine and other naval stores; this grove is in Florida.

years. The wood is used for general construction, barrels, hogsheads and paper pulp.

SLASH PINE is known by a number of other names: Cuban pine, swamp pine, Caribbean pine and southern yellow pine. A rapidly growing tree, it is becoming increasingly popular as an ornamental evergreen. Slash pine is the state tree of Alabama. Its range is more restricted than the preceding pines, being rare north of the Carolinas. Pure stands of slash pine make up the flatwoods of Florida, extending for miles in an open forest growth; the ground cover in these groves is often an exotic understory of palmetto clumps. In general appearance, this pine is similar to longleaf, the tall clean trunks being topped by a crown of shiny green foliage. Its habitat, however, is slightly different, since slash pine prefers low ground and borders of swamps.

The needles of slash pine grow in clusters of two, although occasionally a three-needled cluster can be found. Each needle is almost as long as that of the longleaf, reaching a maximum of twelve inches; they are darker green in color than either longleaf or loblolly. The new growth each season is a "candle" of gray-green, slender as a pencil, terminating the twigs of the slash pine. The contrast of this to the more bushy new growth of the longleaf pine makes it easy to tell the two trees apart in spring. In late winter dark purple, pollen-producing cones and pink seed-producing ones appear. The scales of the seed cones have varnished tips, each armed with a recurved spine. The cones, erect the first season, hang down from the branches when they are mature. The orange or reddish-brown bark consists of overlapping plates which form flat ridges. Slash pine wood is coarse-grained, brittle and resinous; it is used for railroad ties and wood pulp. The chief value of the tree is the resin, which is used for naval stores. Slash pines are tapped like the longleaf, and the crude gum distilled into turpentine and other products. Because of its rapid growth and high resin yield, slash pine has become the most profitable of the turpentine-producing trees.

SHORTLEAF PINE, the state tree of Arkansas, is also known as scrub pine, oldfield pine and rosemary pine.

Ranging from southern New York through the coastal plain to Louisiana and Arkansas, it is a widely distributed evergreen. We can look for this pine when our trail leads across well-drained light sandy soils at higher altitudes. On low, saturated soils shortleaf pine is replaced by loblolly and longleaf. It is the most long-lived of the southern pines, living to be three hundred years of age. An unusually large tree at Morganton, North Carolina, has a girth of 10 feet and is 135 feet high. An attractive lawn tree, shortleaf pine is used as an ornamental in several southern states.

The bark is a cinnamon or yellowish-brown, broken into flat rectangular plates separated by narrow fissures. The needles are usually two in a cluster, although at times clusters can be found with three needles. The term "shortleaf" is misleading, since the needles are short only by comparison with the long-needled southern pines. The needles, three to five inches in length, bluish-green and flexible, form bushy clusters near the ends of the branches. The egg-shaped cones, only a few inches in length, are the smallest of the southern pine cones. The hard and coarse-grained wood is sold in mixtures as southern yellow pine, and used for wood pulp, general construction, chairs and furniture frames.

VIRGINIA PINE is one of the least valuable of the southern pine group, its wood being too brittle and knotty for lumber and the amount of resin being too small for profitable turpentine production. It is also called scrub pine, Jersey pine and spruce pine. This species is a Yankee member of the southern pine group, being common as far north as New Jersey and southern New York, and venturing no farther south than Georgia. A small, flat-topped tree with twisted branches, it can easily be mistaken for a Scotch or pitch pine.

The gray-green foliage consists of two short, stout, often twisted, needles in a cluster. A reliable identification tag is the purplish bloom on the slender new growth, unique in the two-needled pines. Seed-producing cones are purplish, turning brown when mature; they cling closely to the branches, projecting at right angles to them. The scales open during the following three or four years to release the winged seeds. Virginia pine's real value lies in its ability to thrive on dry rocky soil; it forms pure stands on worn-out fields which, without it, would lose the topsoil through lack of vegetation cover. Therefore it is a good erosion control tree.

Bald Cypress

BALD CYPRESS is one of the most picturesque trees of the entire conifer group. It actually is not a true cypress, but a member of the family which also includes the Sequoias (redwoods). Along roadsides as well as on swampy forest trails we can expect this typically southern tree; its home is along the entire coastal margin from southern Virginia to Florida and west to Texas. It is truly an amphibious tree, growing equally well on land or in water. As an ornamental it is hardy as far north as New York; large specimens thrive in the parks in Washington, D.C.

Cypress trees are associated with thoughts of dimly lit passageways through the Everglades, where black water flows silently beneath their limbs draped with Spanish moss; sleepy cottonmouth moccasins coil at their buttressed base; and the alligator's roar can be occasionally heard. It is the tree from which the Seminole Indians hew their dugouts, best means of transportation through the southern swamps.

In winter the bald cypress is leafless, the flattened needles being shed like those of the larch, the other deciduous conifer. Old cypresses have a massive base which flares out in graceful "ribs" and buttresses to brace the tree in the water-soaked soil. The grayish-brown trunks taper gracefully to form a pyramid-shaped crown in young trees, and broad flat-topped crowns in old ones. The patriarch of the cypress clan is a 126-foot tree at Sanford, Florida, which has a circumference of 42 feet. When the cypress is growing in soil which is periodically under water, its base is surrounded by a miniature forest of knob-like growths rising from the horizontal roots, like the stalagmites in the floor of a cavern. These are the cypress "knees" which act as a ventilating device to bring the necessary air to the root system. Otherwise the tree

Bald Cypress.

might suffocate in the saturated soil. In spring, the branches are clothed with light green needles which open out, as the season advances, to form two feathery rows of flat needles along each twig.

The range of the bald cypress today is more restricted than it was in prehistoric time. The living trees are thus a remnant of a race which had its home throughout North America and northern Europe. Long-lived like the sequoias, many cypresses have weathered a thousand years, even though attaining a height of only a hundred feet. The clustered pollen-producing cones occur in purplish tassels, while the seed-producing ones are restricted to the ends of the smaller branches. The mature seed cones are spherical, about an inch in diameter, covered by a few tightly fitting scales. Cypress reproduces by sprout growth from old stumps, as well as by seeds. Thus circular stands of young trees may often be seen, outlining the position of the giant parent tree, long since disappeared.

Cypress wood is extremely durable and resistant to dampness. A well-known use is for shingles and exterior building purposes where long-lasting qualities are important. The present-day stand of cypress is mostly in inaccessible swamps of South Carolina, Florida and Louisiana.

The Oaks

Oaks form the largest group of broad-leaved trees in the southern forests. Like the northern oaks, the pollen-bearing flowers are clustered in drooping catkins and the small female flowers are scattered in groups along the twigs. The fruit is the familiar acorn. Although at times they mingle with the pines, most of the oaks prefer higher and drier ground for their habitats. Throughout the entire southeastern region we can find a few of the species which we met in the northern and central states. White oak extends into Florida, scarlet oak into Georgia and Alabama, and black oak to Texas. Neither scarlet nor black oak is common near the coast.

New species which we are likely to find along southern trails include the southern red oak, swamp chestnut oak, overcup oak; three semi-evergreens, the laurel, willow and water oaks; and the evergreen live oak.

SOUTHERN RED OAK is also known as Spanish oak and water oak. It can be recognized by the sharply pointed lobes of the leaves, which are deciduous. This is a tree of dry hillsides and poor sandy soil, with tall straight trunk and upward-reaching limbs which support a high rounded crown. The range of the southern red oak is from Maryland to Louisiana, and up the lower Mississippi River valley. The largest measured specimen is at Sudley, Maryland; its girth is 23 feet and its height 105 feet.

Foliage of the southern red oak is glossy dark green, with a yellowish or rusty tinge on the underside of the leaves. The leaves are confusing because two types occur, often on the same tree. One has a bell-shaped outline with a wedge-like base and a shallowly three-lobed margin. The other is deeply five-lobed with a scythe-like terminal lobe. In both types the lobes are tipped with sharp bristles. Small acorns are produced which take two years to mature; the spherical striped nut is buried for a third of its length in the scaly saucer-like cup. The coarse-grained wood checks badly, but can be used for inferior grades of construction lumber, crates and boxes.

SWAMP CHESTNUT OAK is another deciduous southern oak; it is also called basket oak because its wood splits into thin strips suitable for making baskets, and cow oak because cattle like to eat the sweet nuts. It is a large oak of lowlands near streams, and occurs from Virginia to Louisiana except along the coast. In Florida it is found in hammocks and wooded ravines in the northern half of

The Southern Oaks.

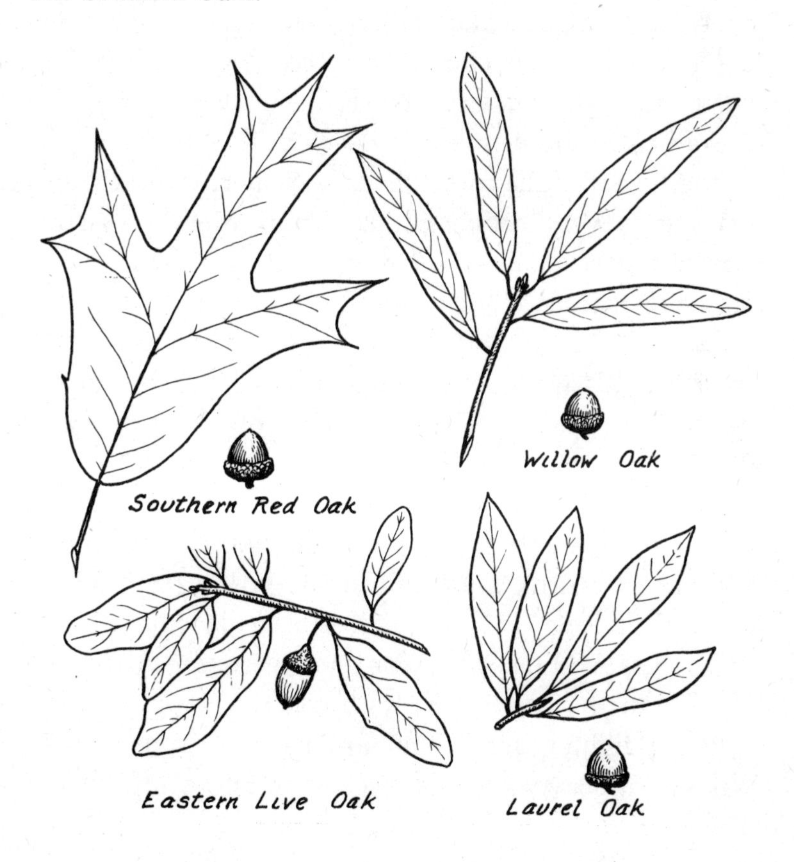

the state. A veteran swamp chestnut oak is growing near Sandhill, Mississippi, which is 30 feet in circumference and 110 feet in height. This species can be recognized by the very large leaves, which may reach a length of eight inches; their scalloped margins have large blunt teeth. The acorns consist of inch-long nuts, egg-shaped and shiny brown, enclosed in thick bowl-like cups. The wood, like that of white oak, is used for flooring, furniture, barrels and woodenware. It is an important timber tree of the southern forest.

LAUREL OAK is an attractive semi-evergreen, often planted as an ornamental in the southern states. The shiny laurel-like leaves remain on the trees until early spring, when they fall and leave the branches bare for a few weeks before the new leaves develop. It is a tree of the southern part of the forest, being rare north of the Carolinas; it is very common throughout Florida. An old specimen at Highlands Hammock State Park, in Florida, has a circumference of 24 feet.

Laurel oak is found where our trail follows stream margins and swamps and leads through thickets of cypress and red maple. The elliptical or oblong leaves usually have a smooth margin, although some may be shallowly lobed; the base is wedge-shaped and the tip pointed. They are dark green, and borne on stout yellow stalks. Laurel oak acorns consist of small dark-brown nuts, a half inch in length, set in a thin saucer-like cup.

WILLOW OAK is another semi-evergreen, often confused with the laurel oak; its leaves, however, are narrower, a lighter green, and are pointed at both ends. Willow oak leaves turn pale yellow in late winter before falling from the branches. This oak can live in poor soil; it is frequently cultivated as a shade and street tree in several southern states. Most willow oaks grow only forty or fifty feet in height, but a remarkable tree near Pelzer, South Carolina, is 21 feet in circumference and 105 feet high.

This oak is sometimes called pin oak because of the many small spur-like branchlets which grow from the main limbs; it is not the same species as the northern pin oak. The acorns have shallow saucer-like cups which cover only the base of the small yellowish or greenish nuts, a prize food of ducks and wild turkeys.

EASTERN LIVE OAK is one of the unforgettable southern trees. Common both in the woods and along city streets, it is a familiar sight from Virginia southward. The same species occurs in Cuba, Central America and Mexico. A short massive main trunk bears large spreading limbs which seem to defy the laws of gravity by extending horizontally for fifty feet or more without support. It is seldom very tall, but the dense rounded crown of one tree will cast a welcome shade over an area the size of a city lot. There are many huge old live oaks lining the approaches to southern plantation homes and arching over the city streets. At Hahnville, Louisiana, stands a massive specimen with a circumference of 35 feet, and a height of 78 feet. The charm of many southern streets and homes is heightened by the arched canopy of live oaks, draped with Spanish moss and carpeted with aerial gardens of ferns and other epiphytes.

Live oak is the state tree of Georgia, and is also the most common broad-leaved tree of Florida, Alabama,

Mississippi and Louisiana. The sharply pointed, elliptical leaves remain on the trees for thirteen months, and are then pushed off by the new brighter-green foliage. Some live oak leaves have smooth margins, slightly rolled under; others bear a few sharp teeth giving them a resemblance to holly leaves. A shiny green on the upper surface, live oak leaves are downy and whitish underneath. Live oak acorns consist of nearly black, egg-shaped nuts an inch in length, partly enclosed in a top-shaped cup. The sweet kernels formed part of the diet of southern Indian tribes, and are today a favorite food of cattle and hogs. The close-grained wood is difficult to work; at one time the junction of the main root with the base of the trunk was prized for making ships' knees. Live oaks are easily transplanted, and grow rapidly, making them a favorite ornamental tree.

The Broad-leaved Deciduous Trees

Many of the deciduous trees of the central and northern states have extended their range to the southern forest. Pignut, mockernut, black walnut, cottonwood, river birch, beech, tulip tree, sycamore and linden are a few which will be encountered in the woods as far south as Florida. The three trees which are included as southern deciduous trees—sweet gum, redbud and persimmon—are also found farther north and to the west. They are described here because they are most abundant in the region populated by the southern forest species, and in some ways seem typically southeastern trees.

SWEET GUM, also known as red gum and star-leaved

gum, grows throughout a large area from southern Connecticut west to Missouri and south to the Gulf of Mexico. It is especially abundant in the lowlands of the southeastern coast. By preference sweet gum is a tree of moist soil, and is generally found near water. Young trees have a straight central trunk with a pyramid-shaped crown, more like a conifer than a broad-leaved tree. Older trees have a more narrow crown, supported by a few, small side branches. In summer sweet gum is easily recognized by the unusual star-shaped leaf which has five or seven pointed lobes. Another identification tag, useful during fall and winter, is the unique fruit, a spherical seed-ball slightly smaller than that of the sycamore, with a spiny appearance caused by the projecting horny tips of the seed capsules. Sweet gum fruits hang on the leafless

Southern Deciduous Trees.

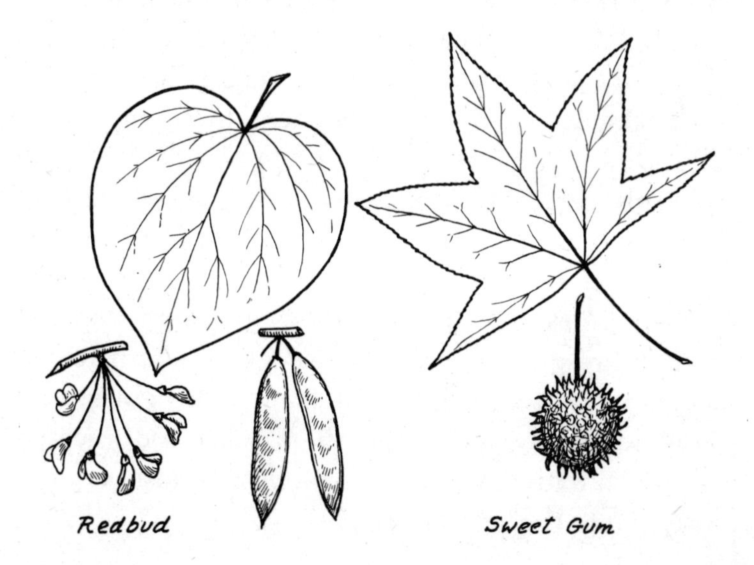

branches throughout the winter. Old trees reach considerable stature; a sweet gum near Florence, South Carolina, has a circumference of 21 feet, a height of 200 feet.

Sweet gum trees have a dark gray, deeply furrowed bark; the smaller side branches and twigs bear corky flattened wings and ridges. The tree gets its name from the yellowish fragrant resin which exudes from the bark. Flowers of both sexes are found on the same tree; the green pollen-producing flowers form erect clusters, but the paler female flowers hang like Christmas tree balls on long stalks. Sweet gum lumber is second only to oak in usefulness and amount cut; most of this comes from the Gulf states and Arkansas. The strong wood has a beautiful grain and luster; it is marketed under the names of satin walnut and Circassian walnut. Gum wood is used for furniture, interior trim and plywood. Free from pests, it is a satisfactory ornamental tree, with foliage which turns many shades of red, orange, and yellow in fall.

RED BUD, or Judas tree, is a small tree which adds color to the southern woodlands in spring. It is native to rich rocky woods from Connecticut to southern New York, west to Minnesota and south to Florida. Before the leaf buds open, the lavender or rose-colored blossoms clothe the branches with pastel tints. Each flower is like a small pea blossom. The trunk and branches are slender, forming a delicate framework for the bright blossoms and rich green foliage. The simple leaves, alternately arranged on the twigs, are heart-shaped. Being a member of the pea family, the fruit is the familiar pod; each pod is thin and flattened, the size of a black locust pod, with a rosy tint to the light brown shell.

The Broad-leaved Evergreens

The southern forests have an evergreen aspect, not only because of the great numbers of pines, but also because of the variety of broad-leaved trees which are also evergreen. The leaves of many of these are leathery, and glossy green on the upper surface. That the forests of the South are so conspicuously evergreen is usually surprising to those who, acquainted only with the trees of the northern states, associate the evergreen habit with a cold climate.

AMERICAN HOLLY is familiar to all Americans as the traditional Christmas decoration. Holly gets its name, in fact, from its association with holy week in early English history. Although found south from New Jersey and Delaware, where holly is the state tree, it is most common

Southern Broadleaved Evergreen Trees.

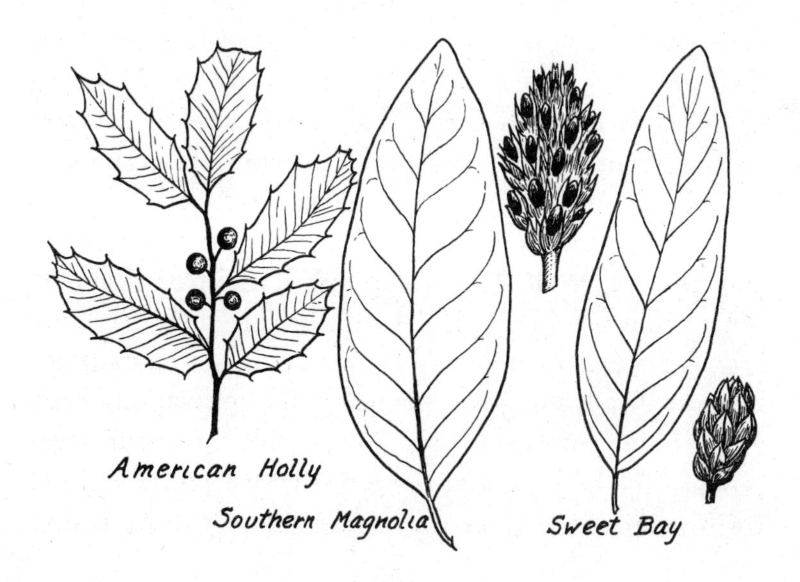

in Virginia and the Carolinas. The largest measured specimen has a circumference of 11 feet and is 50 feet high; this tree grows near Jamestown, Virginia. The glossy green leaves and red berries of the American holly are very similar to English holly, a common ornamental shrub.

The holly tree is a handsome evergreen with a pyramid-shaped compact mass of shiny green foliage. It reaches its best growth in fertile moist soil where hardwoods and pines are often its companions. Bark of young trees is smooth and steel-gray; that of older trees becomes roughened by warty projections. The oval and pointed leaves are borne alternately on the twigs; each leaf is stiff and leathery, with a spiny margin. Holly leaves remain on the branches for three years, then are shed in spring to make way for new growth. The flowers are inconspicuous, consisting of four small white petals; they grow in clusters at the base of the leaves. Since male and female flowers develop on separate trees, some holly trees are pollen-producers and so do not have berries. The bright red berry-like fruit of the female tree contains four nutlets, which take two years to germinate.

Holly wood is white, close-grained and tough; it is used in the manufacture of musical and scientific instruments, and sporting goods. Its greatest value, as a tree, lies in its ornamental use in the Mid-south. Young holly trees are readily transplanted, or can be propagated from cuttings. Certain disadvantages accompany its cultivation, however. Holly plants grow very slowly; only the female trees produce the berries; and these distinctive fruits will not form unless male trees are planted close by. Accessible

Southern Magnolia often reaches heights of a hundred feet, such as this magnificent specimen in Baton Rouge, Louisiana.

roadside holly thickets have been despoiled by excessive picking of the berry-laden branches for decorations. As a result this colorful native tree is fast becoming rare near large cities.

SOUTHERN MAGNOLIA, also known as laurel bay and evergreen magnolia, has been called the most splendid ornamental tree of the American forests. The large shiny leaves reach a length of eight inches, obscuring the branches in a dense crown of deep-green foliage. In blossom, southern magnolia seems more like a rare ornamental than a common forest tree. The large creamy-white flowers, six to eight inches in diameter, are borne singly at the ends of the branches, their delicate coloring intensified by the frame of dark green foliage. Southern magnolia demands a rich soil with ample moisture; it grows near streams and ponds but not actually in the water. This magnificent evergreen can be encountered along forest trails from Virginia to Louisiana; as a street tree it is common as far north as Washington, D.C., and Baltimore. The largest specimen authentically recorded is growing at Brooksville, Florida, with a circumference of 14 feet and a height of 110 feet. Southern magnolia is appropriately the state tree of both Mississippi and Alabama.

The firm gray or brownish bark is broken into thin scales on old trees. The oval leaves have a dark glossy green upper surface but are rusty and hairy on the underside. Each fragrant cup-shaped flower consists of six to ten waxy petals; the flowers are short-lived, rarely lasting more than a few days. Botanists consider the magnolia a representative of the most primitive type of flow-

Southern Magnolia blossoms add an ornamental touch to this splendid native American forest tree of the south.

ering tree. Present-day magnolias seem to be a relic of a much larger pre-glacial group which ranged from Siberia to Greenland, thriving in prehistoric forests side by side with the unusual maidenhair tree. Erect cone-like fruits bear conspicuous scarlet seeds on their surface. The flowers appear from May to June, the fruits in early summer. Magnolia wood has a uniform texture and grain, especially suitable for certain types of furniture and Venetian blinds.

SWEET BAY, also known as swamp magnolia and laurel magnolia, is a smaller coastal plain tree found from New Jersey to Louisiana. In the southern part of the United States it is evergreen. Like sweet gum and willow oak, the sweet bay is a tree of coastal swamps; in Florida it thrives in bayous and along stream margins. The thin, oval or elliptical, leaves are bright shiny green on the upper surface, but are silvery beneath. The leaves are smaller than those of the southern magnolia, rarely being over five inches in length. Sweet bay's fragrant white flowers are somewhat smaller than those of southern magnolia, usually being only two inches in diameter. The fruit is similar to that of the southern magnolia, and bears the same scarlet-colored seeds.

STRANGLING FIG is one of the most unusual of all our native trees. Also known as Florida strangler fig and golden fig, it is found only at the extreme southeastern tip of the United States in the hammocks of southern Florida. Strangling fig begins its life as a seedling perched on the upper branches of other trees, its favorite site being the top of a cabbage palm. As the seedling develops its thick leathery leaves, the strangling fig reveals how it has earned its peculiar name. The roots grow downward like a vine, encircling the trunk of its host with a seemingly harmless but deathly embrace. These aerial roots eventually "strangle" the tree so that, by the time the fig has rooted itself in the ground, its obliging host is dead within the hollow shell of the fig's own trunk. Other aerial roots develop from the branches of old fig trees, growing downwards to form new trunks. Unusual flowers are produced inside a fleshy bag, which becomes the red fruit, similar to the edible fig. A related introduced species, the banyan tree, is grown as a novelty in southern Florida.

RED MANGROVE is another Florida tree with unusual appearance and habits. It is one of the few trees

Strangling Fig begins its life as an epiphyte, then encircles its host (in this case a palm) with a deathly embrace of its aerial roots which finally anchor themselves in the ground. This tree was growing near the Key West highway in Florida.

which can grow with its roots in salt water. As a result it forms a low forest along the southern and southwestern tip of Florida, serving the useful purpose of preventing the shore line from being washed away by the sea. It also forms the salt-water swamp forests in which the nearly-extinct American crocodile makes its home. Mangrove trees are braced at their base by arching aerial roots which act as props for the trunks. Such support is necessary in the unstable water-soaked soil. Good-sized mangrove trees grow only in deep undisturbed soil which is close to the ocean but not exposed to it. Full-grown trees have flat-topped crowns, supported by a tangle of branches. The evergreen leaves are arranged opposite each other; they are thick and leathery like those of the magnolia. Small flowers, with four yellow petals, are produced on long stalks. Mangrove fruits are rusty brown

Red Mangrove trees brace themselves by arching roots which anchor this unusual tree in the salt flats of southern Florida.

and cone-shaped, but often resemble elongated pods because the seeds have the unusual habit of germinating while within the fruit. Each pendant seedling, attached to the fruit, looks like a slender cigar. The young mangrove plant is thus a well-developed plant, able to root itself quickly, when it falls to the shifting mud.

The Palms

We are so well acquainted with pines and spruces, oaks and maples, that we think of American forests in terms of these familiar trees. Few of us, unless we live or have traveled in the South, can imagine palms as native forest trees. The thought of palms usually calls to mind tropical islands and foreign lands. Yet several kinds of palm are as native to the United States as white pine or red maple.

CABBAGE PALM is a far more beautiful tree than the name implies. It is so called because, hidden in the leafy crown, is a large cabbage-like bud considered a tasty morsel by the native Indians. Cabbage palms form groves and thickets in low wet ground near the ocean from South Carolina to Florida and the Gulf states. Like most palms, it has a slender unbranched trunk topped by a cluster of huge compound leaves. Trees seventy and eighty feet in height can be found in protected swamps. A great number of cabbage palms are scattered along the east coast of Florida and in the Everglades; it is a common street and highway tree in the South since it is easy to transplant.

Young trees have rough trunks armed with the bases

of old leaf-stalks; these jagged projections offer a foothold for many such epiphytes as Spanish moss, air plants, and ferns. As trees increase in height, the lower portion of the trunk becomes brown or gray, with smooth or slightly stringy bark. Cabbage palm leaves are huge, consisting of a stiff arching stalk, six or seven feet long, terminated by a fan-shaped blade with radiating ridges, three or four feet in diameter. The leaf is generally torn into shreddy strips by the wind. High winds also uproot the palms easily, since the root system is shallow. Small and fragrant, yellowish-white flowers develop in large drooping clusters at the base of the foliage. These become clusters of black berries with pithy flesh and small brown seeds.

ROYAL PALM is an uncommon tree in the southern forests, being found in only a few places in the Everglades. As its name suggests, it is a regal looking palm with slender smooth trunk reaching skyward for eighty or ninety feet, crowned by a plume-like head of arching leaves. It is a shy member of the moist hammocks, a partner of the red mangrove in our most inaccessible swamps. The easiest trail to royal palm country lies in Royal Palm State Park, near Miami.

The trunks of royal palm are swollen at the base, smooth and gray up to the few green leaf-like sheaths which remain beneath the foliage crown. The leaves, very different in appearance from those of the cabbage palm, are compound, with a central midrib and ribbon-like leaflets arranged on either side like the parts of a feather; each leaf is ten or twelve feet in length. Fragrant small creamy white flowers hang in huge clusters at the base of the leaves, as in the cabbage palm. The blue egg-shaped fruits have a brown flesh and a single light-brown seed. Royal palms are a popular street and park tree in southern Florida towns. Well-known rows of royal palms line main streets of Fort Myers, Palm Beach and Miami.

Cabbage Palms form groves near the ocean along the South Carolina shore.

Coconut Palms today grow "wild" along the shore of eastern Florida.

Chapter 8

ROADSIDE TRAILS IN THE SOUTH

THE SOUTHERN STATES, because of the great number of attractive trees among the native species, are unusually fortunate in having hardy ornamentals which are also native plants. Longleaf, slash, and shortleaf pines make handsome street and park trees, as do southern red oak, laurel oak, willow oak, and live oak. Redbud and dogwood are beautiful roadside flowering trees. Perhaps most attractive of all, and therefore widely used, are American holly and southern magnolia. When the exotic cabbage palm and royal palm are added to this list, it seems as though southern homes would have little need of introduced ornamentals.

The subtropical climate of many of the southern states, and the tropical climate of southern Florida, encourages the growing of many unusual tree immigrants. Some, such as the princess tree and chinaberry, are roadside trees as far north as Virginia and Maryland. Others, especially the palms and their relatives, occur only in the frost-free portions of southern Florida.

Introduced Evergreens

NORFOLK ISLAND PINE is a spruce-like evergreen grown as a street tree in Florida, the Gulf states, and southern California. It is a native of the Norfolk Islands in the South Pacific; its relatives grow in Australia, New Guinea and Chile. It is not a true pine, but a member of the Araucaria family, a small group of evergreens related to the conifers. Norfolk Island pine has a pyramid-shaped crown, with whorled branches and drooping branchlets which are reminiscent of the Norway spruce. The sharply pointed and flattened leaves are lance-shaped, and overlap each other to completely sheath the twig. Each needle is about half an inch in length. In its native home the tree reaches heights of several hundred feet, but specimens in this country rarely exceed fifty feet in height. The seed-cones are spherical and compact, about four inches in diameter.

AUSTRALIAN PINE also is not a pine, but a member of a primitive catkin-bearing group known as the Casuarina family, introduced from Australia. This is a slender, open-topped tree easily mistaken for a pine with a weeping habit. But what at first sight looks like long drooping needles are in reality green leafless stems. Thus the tree is like a cactus in having stems perform photosynthesis in place of foliage leaves, which are absent. Be-

Introduced Southern Evergreen Trees.

cause of the similarity of the jointed leafless stems to the horsetails, a kind of fern, this tree is also known as horsetail tree. Australian pine is grown in Florida, the Southwest, and in southern California wherever the soil is dry and sandy, or so alkaline that other plants cannot grow there. The trees are often planted in rows, the dusty gray-green foliage forming an excellent windbreak for fruit groves and highways. Pollen-producing flowers appear in small greenish erect catkins, but the female flowers are in small rounded clusters. The resulting fruit is a cone-like ball of brown nutlets. Trees fifty feet in height represent the maximum for this rapidly growing tree in the United States.

Introduced Deciduous Trees

PRINCESS TREE, or royal Paulownia, is a native of China which was introduced into the United States in 1824. It is used as an ornamental farther north than most southern trees can survive. Large specimens are growing in many parks in Washington, D.C., and Baltimore. The stout main trunk and few stocky branches bear a dense crown of foliage, with a marked resemblance to a catalpa, for which it is often mistaken. The large heart-shaped leaves arranged opposite each other add to the similarity. Princess tree grows to a height of fifty feet or more, and is an unusually attractive tree when in blossom. Large, showy, erect clusters of violet or pale blue flowers are conspicuous before the leaves appear; when in blossom there is no chance of mistaking this tree. Later in the summer the flowers are replaced by oval capsules about an inch in length and brown in color. These remain on the tree all winter, furnishing another comparison with the catalpa with its bean-like fruits. Princess tree has successfully established itself so that individuals and groves of these trees can be found in the woods on the outskirts of many southern cities. Each flower, several inches in length, has a tubular base and five spreading lobes.

CHINABERRY is an ever-present tree along the highways south of Virginia. It is the poor man's delight, thriving in intense heat and sun-parched soil beside shacks and hovels where few other trees can grow and casting welcome shade beneath its dense foliage. The chinaberry tree was introduced into this country from

Introduced Southern Deciduous Trees.

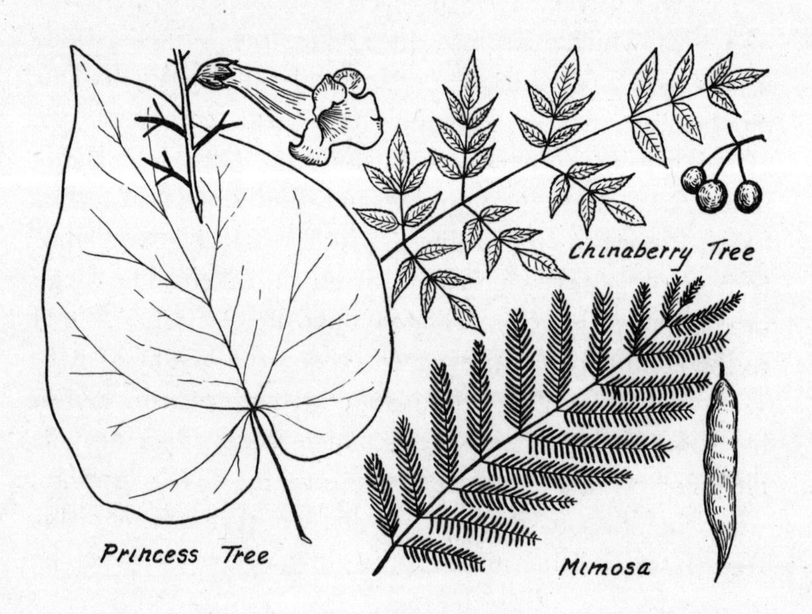

Himalaya in colonial times. When the tree is leafless the main branches can be noticed radiating out from the top of the trunk and bearing clusters of short branches at their tips. This growth habit has given it the name of umbrella tree in the Southwest. It is the only member of the mahogany family commonly grown in the United States. The large leaves—often two feet in length—are doubly compound like those of honey locust; the small leaflets are toothed or lobed, and sharply pointed. Fragrant purple or lilac flowers appear in loose clusters in early spring; each flower consists of five or six petals with a central tube formed by the fusion of the stamens. Clusters of the yellow cherry-like fruits remain on the tree most of the winter, and then form a reliable recognition tag of the chinaberry. Like the princess tree, it has become naturalized in many areas, and can be found in the woods on the outskirts of towns.

MIMOSA, also appropriately known as silk tree and powder-puff tree, is a native of Persia and China. It is a hardy southern ornamental, surviving the winter as far north as Maryland. Its subtropical ancestry is suggested by the filmy and fernlike foliage; the large doubly compound leaves are divided into hundreds of small leaflets. Mimosa is a low-growing tree with spreading branches and a characteristic flat-topped crown. In flower, mimosa is a showy tree. The profusion of delicate pink blossoms in compact clusters have undoubtedly suggested the name "powder-puff" tree. The rich green foliage provides a pleasing background to the pastel tints of the flowers. The fruits are light tan pods, a few inches in length, which remain on the limbs during the winter.

ROYAL POINCIANA is the most showy of all flowering trees; this is reflected in two of its common names: peacock flower and flamboyant tree. Like the mimosa it is a member of the pea family, and thus bears pods when in fruit; these are huge and brown, almost a foot in length. A native of Madagascar, it was introduced into the Southwest and southern California as well as into southern Florida. It is a low-growing tree with spreading branches and a flat top; it retains its leaves except for a few weeks in early spring. The fernlike doubly compound leaves consist of many small oval leaflets. Each flower, produced in summer, is several inches in diameter and has bright scarlet petals, one with a yellow stripe. The flowers are borne in small clusters, adding a striking accent to a tree which is attractive even for its foliage alone.

Some Palms and Their Relatives

COCONUT PALM grows "wild" along the shore-line of the entire southeastern coast of Florida, but is thought to have been introduced by early explorers. It is planted as an ornamental along many streets and around many homes in southern Florida. Coconut palms, like other palms, have tall slender trunks crowned by a cluster of huge compound leaves. Its usual pose is leaning, as if unable to resist the continual winds and hurricanes which buffet it. For the same reason the windswept crown presents a ragged and torn appearance. Each drooping leaf is fifteen to twenty feet in length, with strap-shaped leaflets arranged feather-like along the midrib. At the

The Banana Tree is a relative of the palms, with huge leaves and the familiar fruit. This fruiting tree was photographed in New Orleans.

base of the leaves occur branching clusters of white or yellow flowers, inconspicuously small. The fruit is the familiar coconut, ten to twenty in each cluster. The meat of the coconut is the plant embryo with the solid portion of the stored food; the milk is a rich mixture of sugars and oils, also a reserve food for the young embryo.

Coconut palms are widely distributed trees, being found along seacoasts throughout the tropics. They have been called the most valuable trees in the world because of the variety of products they provide. The name "cocos" means monkey in Portuguese, and refers to the monkey-like face which the three "eyes" give to the end of the coconut. Coconut is one of the few fruits adapted for dispersal by water; the seed, which is the commercial coconut, is surrounded by thick fibrous and waterproof layers which act as a life-preserver to keep the fruit afloat for a long time. When the coconut comes to rest against the bank of a stream, it germinates to become a coconut palm. The native home of the coconut palm is not definitely known. Some botanists trace its origin to South America, others to the South Pacific islands. Whatever its ancestry, it adds a tropical flavor to many Florida beaches.

BANANA TREE, sometimes incorrectly called banana palm, is really not a tree, but a huge perennial herb even though it reaches a stature of ten or fifteen feet. Originally a native of the Malay region, it has been cultivated for years in India and was well known to the ancient Greeks. Easily injured by frost, it is grown successfully only as an ornamental in tropical portions of the United States. The commercial banana crop comes from Jamaica, Costa Rica, Cuba and Honduras. The stem is underground, and what looks like a trunk is a series of overlapping leaf-bases, supporting the few huge feather-veined leaves. These are often a foot in width and six feet long. Such large leaf surfaces are easily torn and shredded by winds and storms, so that old banana leaves are rarely intact. The trees have become naturalized in the warmer parts of Florida, to become a roadside weed in moist protected hollows. The flowers are borne in a huge drooping cluster which continues to grow while flowers and fruit are forming. Near the tip of this cluster may be found the large purplish bracts beneath which the flowers are hidden. Farther back on the stalk are the newly-formed small bananas, pointing upward. Within

Traveler's Tree has a crown of flattened leaves, their bases overlapping as if braided, and often a reservoir of rain water.

each banana are small black specks, which are the sterile seeds; banana trees are propagated by root sprouts. Each tree bears one bunch of bananas and then dies; the new plants arise from the base of the old one.

TRAVELER'S TREE, sometimes also called incorrectly a palm, is a member of the banana family introduced from Madagascar. This relationship is evident from the similar size and shape of the huge leaves. Traveler's tree grows to be twenty feet in height, and is a spectacular plant. The leaves form a flattened fan-like mass of foliage, with the bases of the leaf-stalks overlapping each other in symmetrical fashion. These leaf bases are enlarged so that they collect great quantities of rain-water; when the leaf-stalks are cut, the water often spurts out as if a faucet has been opened. Travelers have supposedly been saved from dying of thirst by finding this hidden source of water, hence the name of the tree.

These are but a few of the many interesting tropical and subtropical trees which have been introduced into Florida and adjacent states. Few other parts of the country can boast such an interesting and varied tree population. Once you have visited the subtropical portion of the southern forest area, you will agree that the tree members are unique and colorful. It is clear that one factor which makes natural history so fascinating in the United States is the great range in living conditions from the alpine ridges of the New England mountains to the tropical mangrove swamps of southern Florida.

Chapter 9

TRAILS IN THE ROCKY MOUNTAIN FOREST

THE ROCKY MOUNTAIN region is a high plateau with a snow-covered mountainous backbone, where an empire of evergreen trees clothe the slopes of the peaks from their lowermost sheltered valleys to the upper limits of tree growth. These conifer forests reach altitudes of 11,000 feet in the central and southern portions of the Rockies. As one drives up Pikes Peak in Colorado (elevation 14,000 feet), he notices that the distance of the last few thousand feet of altitude is devoid of trees. The farther north one travels the lower one finds timber line; in the mountains of Arizona and New Mexico the upper limit of trees is found near 12,500 feet, but farther north in Idaho and Montana, trees cannot grow at an altitude of more than 9,000 feet.

The Rocky Mountain forest occupies a most scenic part of the country where the wild life is preserved for future generations of Americans in many national parks and forests. Glacier National Park, in northwestern Montana, lies at the northern edge of this forest area. Here our trail leads through miles and miles of Engelmann spruce, alpine fir, Douglas fir, and lodgepole pine. To the south in Yellowstone National Park, the forest community is made up of the same trees but, at the lower altitudes where most visitors spend their time, lodgepole pine is the most common conifer. At nearby Grand Teton National Park lodgepole pine also is the usual tree on the floor of the valleys; but Engelmann spruce, thriving on the rich soil along the streams, grows to be the largest tree of the park.

In the central portion of the Rockies, in Colorado, lies Rocky Mountain National Park. Forest trails in this part of the forest, on the lower slopes, lead through open groves of magnificent ponderosa pine mixed with Douglas fir and lodgepole pine. The silvery shafts of blue spruce crowd along the streams, while on the higher slopes grow the hardy Engelmann spruce and alpine fir. But at 12,000 feet these trees become gnarled and stunted, carrying on a life-and-death struggle at timber line to survive in this rigorous environment.

In Grand Canyon National Park, in Arizona, we find the evergreen community typical of the southern Rockies. Two trees dominate this arid region at altitudes below 6,000 feet: Utah juniper and pinyon. As the trail winds upward, it passes through groves of stately ponderosa pine mixed with Douglas fir and white fir. At still higher altitudes, between 8,000 and 10,000 feet, we find the same Engelmann spruce-alpine fir belt which extended to timber line in the central Rockies.

The deciduous trees are in the minority. Quaking aspen is the most common broad-leaved tree, often found in extensive belts around the lower slopes of the mountains. Live oaks, stunted willows, shrubby birches and several species of cottonwood also occur. But the Rocky Mountain forest is conspicuously one of abundant conifers, many of them growing to huge size. As conifers, they can be recognized by their habit of producing their seeds in woody cones, and by their small needle-like or scale-like leaves.

The Pines

The pines have distinctive foliage, consisting of slender needle-like leaves grouped in clusters of two, three or five. The cones of pines are generally larger than those of the other conifers, varying in size from a few inches to sixteen inches. *Five* needles in a cluster identify the western white pine; ponderosa pine usually has *three* needles in a cluster; and paired needles (*two* in a cluster) are typical of lodgepole and pinyon pines.

WESTERN WHITE PINE is a tree of the Pacific Northwest, being found in Idaho, Montana, and along the Pacific Coast. In altitude, its range is from 2,000 to 5,000 feet in the northern part of its home, and up to 10,000 feet in the Sierras of California. This pine can be recognized from a distance by its slender tapering shaft of bluish-green foliage; its short branches droop gracefully and then curve upward at their tips. It is more like a spruce in general appearance than a pine. At Bovill, Idaho, a western white pine has a circumference of 26 feet and has reached a height of 207 feet.

As in the eastern white pine, the needles are grouped in clusters of five, but each needle is thicker and more rigid than its eastern relative, and only two to four inches in length. The bark, broken into rectangular blocks, is usually light gray but becomes cinnamon-brown when growing in exposed situations. Purple seed-producing cones appear on the higher branches, becoming cylindrical and brown when mature. These stand erect until pollinated, when they change their positions and hang downward on the branches. Western white pine cones are very large, reaching lengths of ten to twelve inches. Being slim and slightly curved, they are responsible for the local name of "finger-cone pine." Western white pine is an important timber tree, since its wood is harder and stronger than eastern white pine; it is used for construction lumber, interior trim, and window and door frames. It is one of the few western pines which is grown as an ornamental; it is not surprising that it has been selected as the state tree of Idaho.

Rocky Mountain Pines.

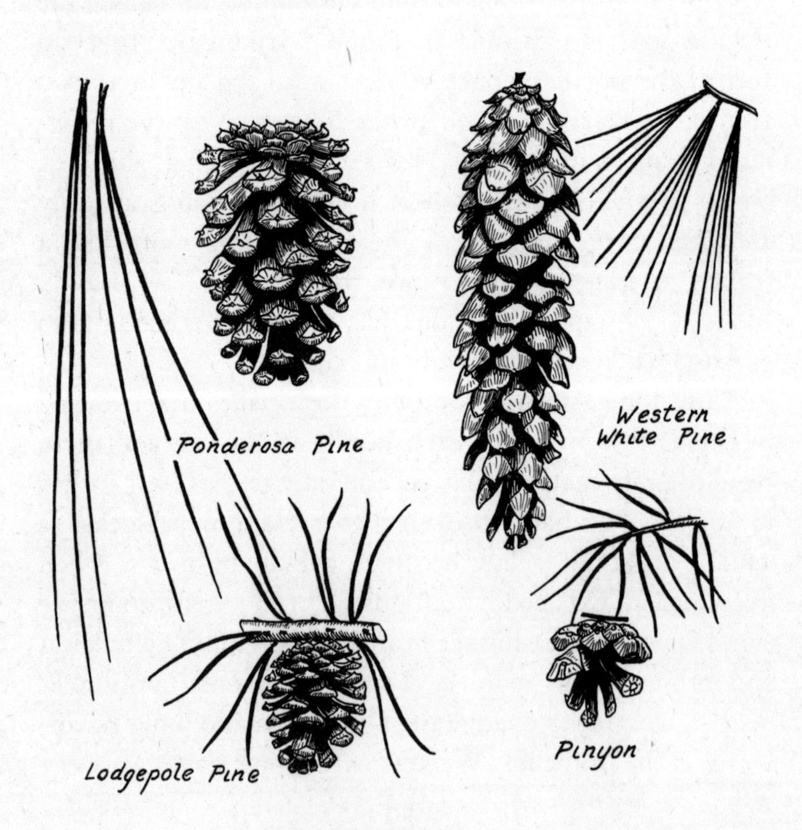

PONDEROSA PINE, or western yellow pine, is one of the most familiar trees in our western national parks, and is the state tree of Montana. It grows from the Dakotas south to Texas and west to the Pacific Coast. This valuable native pine was discovered by members of the Lewis and Clark Expedition while exploring the Missouri River in 1804. Ponderosa pine is an impressive tree with a massive trunk, often free of branches for fifty or seventy-five feet, topped by an open crown of dark green foliage. The trunk is an excellent recognition feature, since its bright orange-yellow bark is conspicuous among the darker grays and browns of the other conifers. The thick bark separates into large flat-topped plates covered by papery layers and scales. Ponderosa pine thrives on well-drained slopes from 6,000 to 10,000 feet altitude. Trees several hundred feet in height have been reported by lumbermen, but the largest measured specimen, growing near Lapine, Oregon, is 162 feet high and has a circumference of 27 feet.

The foliage forms heavy brush-like clusters at the ends of the branches; the long needles, six to eight inches in length, are ordinarily grouped in three's, although clusters with two needles are occasionally found. Seed-producing cones are purplish-green when first formed, and three to six inches in length; later they become brown and hang downward from the branches. Ponderosa pine is second only to Douglas fir in value as a timber tree. The hard, strong wood is fine-grained, and can be used for general building purposes, furniture and veneers. A count of the growth rings in stumps reveals ages of three hundred to five hundred years for many ponderosa pines.

LODGEPOLE PINE can well be considered the most common conifer of the northern Rockies, since throughout the Northwest it can be found along almost every trail from sea level to altitudes of 10,000 feet. It is also very common in the Pacific Coast states. Its name refers to the use of young saplings as poles for the lodges and tepees of the Indians. Other names for this tree are shore pine, black pine and knotty pine. When growing in groves, the trees are tall and slender, with short rounded crowns. Lodgepole pine generally grows to heights of sixty and seventy feet. An unusually large tree, growing in the Sierra National Forest of California, has a circumference of 19 feet and is 109 feet high.

The yellowish-green foliage consists of stout and twisted needles, an inch or two in length, arranged in pairs. Thin scaly bark, pale brown or gray, is distinctively separated into small oblong plates. The inner bark was used by Indians for food and also for making baskets. The hard and straight-grained wood makes lodgepole pine lumber useful for general construction purposes and for railroad ties and fence posts. Most of the trees cut for lumber come from Colorado and Wyoming. The egg-shaped and lopsided seed cones are small compared with the other pines only an inch or two in length. Cones hang in clusters of a dozen or more, and often remain closed on the branches for several years.

PINYON, or nut pine, a low-growing pine of the southern Rockies, forms open groves on the dry foothills and mesa slopes at altitudes of 5,000 to 8,000 feet throughout Colorado, Utah, Arizona and New Mexico. The name was given this pine by early Spanish explorers.

Its large edible seeds or "pinyon nuts" were formerly an important staple in the diet of the Indians of the Southwest, who baked them in order to preserve them for storage. Appropriately, pinyon is the state tree of New Mexico. The regular, though natural, spacing of pinyon stands reminds an Easterner of old apple orchards. Average trees are only fifteen or twenty feet in height; growth is so slow that it is possible to find trees two hundred years old that are less than a foot in diameter.

Short twisted trunks and scraggly branches support a low rounded crown of yellowish-green foliage. The sharply pointed, paired needles are only an inch in length; when first formed they add a bright bluish-green tint to the tree. Bark of pinyon is reddish-brown, with shallow irregular ridges covered with scaly section. The seed-bearing cones, purple when young, develop into egg-shaped shiny brown cones an inch or two in length, usually at the tips of the branches.

The Firs

Next in importance to the pines, throughout the Rocky Mountain forests, are the firs and spruces. These conifers differ from the pines in having shorter, flattened or square needles arranged singly along the branches instead of in clusters. Firs and spruces can also be recognized by their symmetrical and graceful pyramidal shape. Firs have flattened needles which often form a two-ranked or flat spray; spruces have stiffer needles which grow out on all sides of the branches, giving a bottle-brush effect.

GRAND FIR is also known as lowland fir because of

its abundance at low altitudes where it attains its best growth along the moist banks of streams. It is also called white fir because of the chalky areas which develop on the otherwise gray-brown smooth bark. Grand fir is the tallest of our native firs, with trees reaching reported heights of two hundred and fifty and three hundred feet. It can be recognized by its tall slender column of foliage, with the lower branches sweeping downward and reaching to the ground; higher branches droop gracefully and then turn upward at their tips.

The glossy yellowish-green foliage consists of flattened needles which are silvery white on the under surface. Each needle is an inch or two in length and grooved on the upper surface; the rounded tip is usually notched. Bark of old trees becomes ridged and dark brown. Grand

Rocky Mountain Firs.

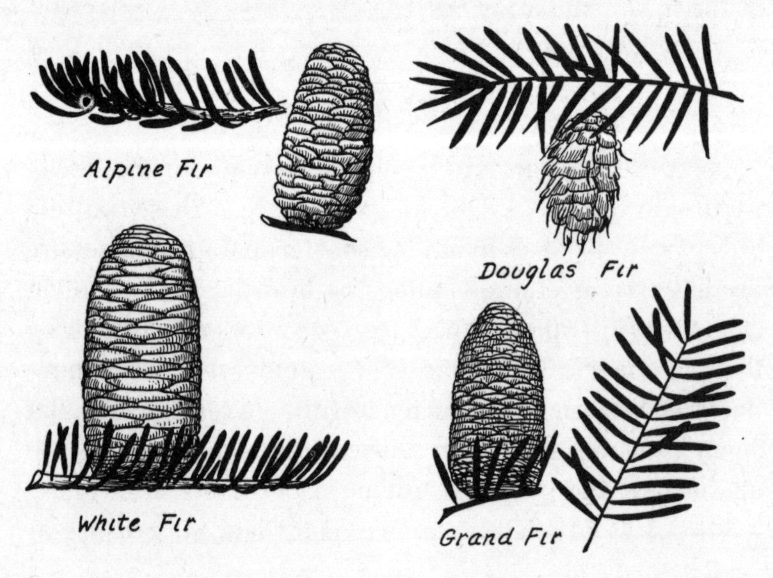

fir wood is too brittle and weak to be of use as construction lumber; its chief commercial value is as wood pulp. The cylindrical seed cones, two to four inches in length, stand upright on the upper branches. After the seeds are dispersed the cone scales fall off, leaving a spike-like core attached to the branch during the winter.

WHITE FIR is a tree of the southern Rockies and therefore will be found where our trail leads across lower mountain slopes in Colorado, Utah, Arizona and New Mexico. It grows on north slopes, but does best in the rich moist soil of river valleys. A tree in Plumas National Forest of California (white fir grows also in Oregon and California) has attained a circumference of 22 feet, and is 213 feet in height. Although the old foliage is yellowish-green, the new growth is pale and whitish, being responsible for its name. Other local names are white balsam, balsam fir and silver fir.

Trees grown in the open have a broad base, tapering to a pointed tip. The dense foliage clothes the numerous symmetrical whorls of branches of which the lowermost ones reach the ground. The flattened needles are bluntly pointed, one to three inches in length, and grow outward at a distinct angle to the twigs. White fir cones are cylindrical and stand erect on the branches; each cone is three to five inches in length. Olive-green or purple when first formed, they become dark gray or brown when mature. Like the grand fir, the core of the cone remains on the branches all winter. The white, straight-grained wood has a fine texture, and is suitable for construction, interior trim, and general building use. This attractive species has become popular as an ornamental in the East.

ALPINE FIR is found only where our trail takes us to the "high country" of the Rockies. This mountaintop tree is typical of forests at 4,000 to 10,000 feet, and is a common timber-line species. It ranges from Idaho and Montana southward to the high peaks of Arizona and New Mexico. The slender spires of blue-green foliage are easily recognized, as is their habit of growing in cool moist locations. Old trees seldom reach great stature because of the rigorous conditions under which they live. Individuals seventy-five feet high are good-sized trees for alpine fir. Specimens with a diameter of two feet, at high altitudes, may well be two centuries old. Like other firs, the lower branches often sweep earthward and cover the base of the trunk.

Old foliage is a blue-green color but the new growth has a striking silvery tinge. The flat and blunt-tipped needles, an inch in length, often curve around the twig to point upward. Alpine fir bark is flinty gray or chalk white, marked by the usual fir resin blisters. Purple seed-bearing cones stand erect on the branches in the upper part of the tree; each cone is cylindrical, two to four inches in length. Because of its inaccessible location, alpine fir has been of little value as a timber tree.

DOUGLAS FIR is our second largest forest tree, being exceeded in height and girth only by the Sequoias. In terms of total stand, it is the most abundant of our timber trees. Douglas fir is known by a number of other, and somewhat confusing, names: Douglas spruce, Douglas yew, red fir and Oregon pine. There is an excuse for this, however, since the tree is botanically a puzzle. Even its scientific name means "false hemlock with a yew-like leaf." It actually is neither a spruce nor a fir, but a genus by itself. Douglas fir is a magnificent forest tree of the entire Rocky Mountain region and of the Pacific Coast; it was discovered on Vancouver Island in 1791 and later introduced into Europe by the Scottish traveler, David Douglas. Often two hundred feet in height, forest-grown trees frequently have the first hundred feet of trunk straight and clear of all branches. A tree in Olympic National Park, Washington, has a girth of 53 feet and a height of 221 feet. Douglas fir reaches its greatest size and abundance near sea level along the coast of Washington and Oregon. Old trees are estimated to be one thousand years of age. Young Douglas firs are broadly pyramid-shaped and symmetrical, but with age they develop a narrow tapering crown and a clean lower trunk; the horizontal branches often bear numerous drooping branchlets. The foliage is rich dark green.

The soft flat needles, which resemble those of a fir, are about an inch in length and grow all around the twig in the manner of spruces. Each needle is grooved on the upper surface, and marked by two lengthwise lines on the underside. Douglas fir bark is deeply furrowed and reddish-brown; it is unusually thick, in some cases ten or twelve inches deep. Oval cones, two to four inches in length, hang from the branches; they possess a special identification tag in the form of three-pointed bracts which project beyond the cone scales, giving the cone a fringed appearance. The yellowish or reddish tinted wood is light, strong and easily worked; its wide use for building purposes is well known. The trees cut for lumber come mostly from Oregon and Washington. It serves as an excellent ornamental tree, since it has an attractive appearance and yet can grow in a wide range of rainfall and soil conditions. Douglas fir is the state tree of Washington.

The Spruces

The spruces are similar to the firs in having tapering, spire-like foliage crowns, but their needles are four-angled and thus are usually stiff and pointed. A needle-covered branch of spruce is more prickly to touch than a spray of fir needles.

ENGELMANN SPRUCE is named for Dr. Engelmann, a famous American botanist of St. Louis who first described the tree in 1863. The narrow pyramid-shaped crown of dark blue-green foliage is a common sight along forest trails at high altitudes from Idaho and Montana southward to the Colorado plateau. They are frequently the last trees to be encountered where the trail approaches timber line. This western spruce occurs also in the Cascade Mountains of Oregon and Washington. Throughout its range it can be found at altitudes of 6,000 feet and higher. The drooping lower branches, from which hang many small branchlets, remind us of the eastern Norway spruce. In sheltered locations trees reach a height of a hundred feet and live to be five hundred years old. In the Cache National Forest of Idaho, a specimen has been measured with a circumference of 19 feet and a height of 104 feet. At timber line, however, trees four feet high may be a hundred years of age.

The soft needles of Engelmann spruce are about an

inch in length, with a definitely disagreeable odor when crushed; new growth has a silvery tinge. The dark purplish or reddish-brown bark is covered with scaly sections. Seed-producing cones are scarlet when young, and develop into cylindrical light brown cones one to three inches in length. The light, fine-grained wood is used for interior trim; it was a popular wood for construction of early types of airplanes.

BLUE SPRUCE, one of our most attractive native evergreens, has become well known throughout the East as an ornamental tree. Also known as Colorado spruce, it is the state tree of both Colorado and Utah. Its native home is in Colorado, together with adjacent portions of Utah, Arizona and New Mexico. Here, where the trail winds along stream banks and over moist lowlands, we find groves of blue spruce, the silvery blue spires rising from the slopes as if they had been landscaped by man. The compact pyramid-shaped crown is familiar, as is the crisp gray-blue foliage of young trees. Older trees become a darker green, and lose the lower whorls of branches. A

Rocky Mountain Spruces.

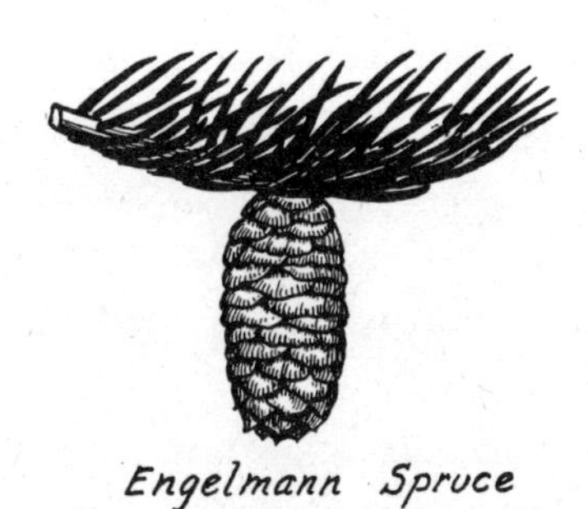

tree in Gunnison National Forest of Colorado is 123 feet high, and has a circumference of 11 feet. Pure stands of blue spruce are rare, the tree usually mingling with Douglas fir, Engelmann spruce and occasionally alpine fir.

The needles of blue spruce are stiff and sharply pointed, about an inch in length. The frosted appearance of the foliage is due to a powdery substance on the surface of the needles which can easily be rubbed off. The foliage can be distinguished from that of Engelmann spruce by the less obnoxious odor when crushed. Another difference lies in the bark, which has vertical ridges, seldom found in Engelmann spruce. The greenish-purple cylindrical cones stand erect until after pollination, when they become light brown and drooping. Being two to four inches long, they are twice the size of Engelmann spruce cones. The brittle and knotty wood is of little commercial value; the greatest importance of the blue spruce is as an ornamental and for this use nurserymen have developed many striking varieties.

A Deciduous Western Conifer

In addition to these pines, spruces and firs which we have discovered along our Rocky Mountain forest trails, we should mention a common deciduous conifer, the western larch. The needles, like those of the pines, grow in clusters, but are much shorter and more delicate in appearance; they turn bright yellow before being shed in autumn.

WESTERN LARCH, also known as mountain larch and western tamarack, is the western counterpart of the common larch of the eastern states and is similar in appearance. Western larch, discovered in Washington by David Douglas in 1826, grows at moderate altitudes throughout the Pacific Northwest, from Idaho and Montana to Washington and Oregon. This species, the largest and most valuable of all our native larches, reaches its greatest size and abundance in Montana. A record-sized tree, growing in Kootenai National Forest of Montana, has a circumference of 24 feet and is 120 feet high. Although sometimes found in pure stands, it usually grows in company with Douglas fir, lodgepole pine and Engelmann spruce.

The tall thin crown of foliage resembles a spruce or fir, but is distinctive by its more open branching and the light airy green of the needles. Each needle is flattened and pointed, about an inch in length; the needles are clustered in groups of thirty or forty. The reddish-brown bark, becoming deeply furrowed with age, is covered by overlapping rounded scales. The bark, several inches thick, protects the western larch against fire, the ever-present menace in our great national forests. Young seed-producing cones are purple or red; they develop into brown broadly egg-shaped cones an inch in length, with bracts projecting beyond the cone scales. The cones fall from the branches in autumn. Larch wood is the heaviest of all the conifers, and is used for railroad ties, poles, posts and some construction lumber.

The Scale-leaved Evergreens

All of the trees which we have so far described for

the Rocky Mountain forest have had needle-like leaves. The foliage of some other western evergreens consists of minute scale-like leaves in place of needles. These tiny leaves overlap each other to completely cover the twigs. In an earlier chapter we became familiar with two eastern trees of this group—red cedar and arbor vitae. In the Rocky Mountain forest two common scale-leaved evergreen trees are Arizona cypress and Utah juniper.

ARIZONA CYPRESS is a true cypress and therefore not a close relative of the bald cypress of the southeastern swamps. Its closest botanical relation is the ornamental Italian cypress, familiar to gardeners, which is not native to the United States. Arizona cypress, which is the state tree of Arizona, is a small tree found on the mountains and in the canyons of southern Arizona and New Mexico, between altitudes of 4,500 and 8,000 feet. On dry and exposed hillsides it is a low stunted tree, but in favored surroundings it grows to a medium size. A speciman in Coronado National Forest near Tucson, Arizona, has a circumference of 17 feet and is 91 feet high.

The straight and rapidly tapering trunk is almost completely covered by the dense, pale-green foliage which forms a tapering crown. The small leaves form rectangular sprays, which have a disagreeable odor when crushed. Bark of old trees, grayish-brown in color, becomes shredded and fibrous. Small, spherical seed-producing cones, about an inch in diameter, are attached to the branches by short stalks. Each cone consists of six to eight scales, each with a central spine. Cones remain on the trees for many years.

UTAH JUNIPER is the most common evergreen tree

of Utah, Nevada, Colorado and Arizona. It is able to grow where few other trees can thrive, on rocky and dry mesas and canyon slopes, at altitudes of 5,000 to 8,000 feet. Utah juniper is most familiar as the tree which forms park-like groves along the south rim of the Grand Canyon. It is a short-trunked tree with a bushy habit and irregular twisted branches, contributing a picturesque feature to the southwestern landscape. Most individuals are twenty feet or less in height; growth is so slow in this arid region that it often requires two hundred years to produce a tree six inches in diameter.

The pale yellow-green foliage consists of twigs surrounded by overlapping series of the scale-like leaves; crushed branches have a pungent and aromatic odor. The gray bark is strongly ridged and separates into thin shreddy strips. Unlike most conifers, the male and female cones are found on different trees. The fleshy scales of the seed-producing cone unite to form a berry-like spherical fruit the size of a small pea, and enclosing one or two seeds. A whitish bloom conceals the reddish-brown color of the berry. Juniper berries are eaten by Indians as well as by birds. The wood, like that of the Arizona cypress, is of little commercial value because of the small size of the tree.

The General Sherman tree in Sequoia National Park is a giant Sierra Redwood with a diameter of 36 feet and a height of 272 feet.

Chapter 10

TRAILS IN THE PACIFIC COAST FOREST

THE PACIFIC COAST states provide the best combination of rainfall, humidity and temperature for the development of giant trees to be found anywhere in the United States. It is therefore a fitting climax to have our forest trails end among the magnificent conifers of California, Oregon and Washington. Many of these wooded areas lie within the boundaries of national and state parks. Thus our trails can combine an interest in natural history with an appreciation of the most scenic areas of the West Coast.

Mt. Rainier National Park in Washington is typical of the northern portion of the Pacific Coast forest. At low altitudes the trees include Douglas fir, western hemlock, and western red cedar. Several species of fir and western white pine grow at higher altitudes, and at the upper limit of tree growth—which is 7,500 feet on Mt. Rainier—alpine fir is again the common timber-line tree. Thus many of the conifers in the northern portion of this area are the same as those in Montana and Idaho.

Crater Lake National Park in Oregon gives us a picture of the forest community in the middle Pacific Coast at altitudes of 5,000 to 7,000 feet. The lowest forest belt is a mixture of broad-leaved and evergreen trees. This zone includes such new species as madrona, Pacific dogwood, bigleaf maple, Pacific yew and western hemlock. In the forests at higher altitudes we find again such Rocky Mountain trees as lodgepole pine, western white pine, Douglas fir, Engelmann spruce and alpine fir. With these grow the new species, sugar pine and incense cedar.

Near the seacoast of California, in the low coastal ranges, grows the coast redwood, one of two species of Sequoia. A vast domain of these giant trees extends for almost five hundred miles from Monterey, California, to southwestern Oregon. The famous Redwood Highway passes through this redwood empire, much of which is fortunately state- or federal-owned land. Many state and county parks protect these groves of unique American trees. Best known is Humboldt Redwoods State Park in northern California. It is here, at Dyerville Flats, that the world's tallest tree is growing, a redwood known as the Founder's Tree, 364 feet high. Other redwood parks accessible to visitors include Muir Woods National Monument just north of San Francisco, and California State Redwood Park (better known as Big Basin) south of San Francisco. No visit to California is complete without a day spent among these never-to-be-forgotten redwood groves. On the western slopes of the Sierras grows another species of Sequoia, known as the Sierra redwood or Big Tree. Yosemite, Sequoia and General Grant National Parks are representative of this portion of the Pacific Coast forest.

As we explore the many trails in Yosemite, we find a variety of trees, from those inhabiting the hot, dry lowlands, to the dense forests on the cool, moist slopes above the rim of Yosemite Valley at altitudes of 8,000 feet or more. As we approach the park, the highway takes us through a foothill region where the common trees are scattered groves of digger pine and live oak. Higher up, on the floor of Yosemite Valley, the forest includes impressive groves of ponderosa pine and incense cedar. Higher still grow various firs, pines and hemlock. Above the rim of the valley is located the well-known Mariposa Grove of "big trees," including several hundred giants over ten feet in diameter. The Grizzly Giant, a veteran of the grove, is well over three thousand years of age. Another famous Sequoia in this grove is the Wawona Tree, through which a tunnel 8 feet wide and 26 feet long was cut for the roadway over seventy years ago.

Also on the western slopes of the Sierras lies Sequoia National Park, a forest of some six hundred square miles set aside to preserve forever the justly famous trees. The thirty-two groves in the park contain half of all the known Sierra redwoods. Tallest is the General Sherman tree, whose estimated age of four thousand years makes it the oldest living thing on earth. Growing with the Sequoias are sugar pine, lodgepole pine, western white pine, white fir, red fir and incense cedar.

The Pines

In our exploration of the eastern and southern forests we discovered that pines are the most numerous of all the conifers. In these forests we became acquainted with eleven species. We learned to identify five other species in the Rocky Mountain region. Here in the Pacific Coast forest we shall meet four additional kinds of pine. Thus throughout the United States we have encountered twenty different species of pine along our forest trails. In the woods of California, Oregon and Washington some of the Rocky Mountain species have established themselves: western white, ponderosa and lodgepole pines. With these grow additional species not found east of the Pacific Coast states. Of these, sugar pine has *five* needles in a cluster, and Jeffrey pine and digger pine have *three* needles in a cluster.

SUGAR PINE has the distinction of being the tallest of our pines and producer of the biggest cones. A tree in Stanislaus National Forest with a height of 200 feet is 31 feet in circumference. Many sugar pine cones can be found which are a foot in length, while occasional specimens are twenty inches long. Sugar pine gets its name from the white resin blisters which exude an unusual sweet secretion from injured places in the bark. This pine

Pacific Coast Pines.

grows in the coast ranges at altitudes of 1,000 to 2,000 feet, and at altitudes of 7,000 to 9,000 feet in the Sierras. A giant among the pines, it was discovered in Oregon in 1825 by David Douglas, evidence of whose exploration and travels we have met before.

The straight trunk of the sugar pine often rises fifty feet or more before the first branch; deep bluish-green foliage forms a broad and attractive crown, often flattened at its summit like an eastern white pine. Sugar pine needles, three to four inches in length, are stout and stiff and occur five in a group. The bark of old trees is furrowed into irregular ridges, covered with purplish or reddish scales. Greenish-purple seed cones stand erect the first year they are formed; as they mature the second year they change position and hang downward. Each large edible seed is the size of a grain of corn, and has a wing several inches long. Sugar pine wood is soft and easily worked, like eastern white pine; it is likewise suitable for interior trim, general building purposes and construction.

JEFFREY PINE, also known as bull pine and black pine, so closely resembles ponderosa pine, with which it usually grows, that the two are often confused. Like sugar pine, Jeffrey pine is almost exclusively a California conifer, its range barely extending into southern Oregon. It frequently becomes a large tree in the Sierras; an individual near Idyllwild, California, has a measured circumference of 25 feet and a height of 130 feet. Short, spreading branches often droop at their tips. Because of its symmetry and bluish-green foliage, Jeffrey pine is often grown as an ornamental.

The needles, arranged three in a cluster, are five to

ten inches in length, which is the same as ponderosa pine needles. They are more blue-green then those of ponderosa pine, however, whose foliage has a yellowish-green tint. The purplish-brown bark becomes fissured and split into large irregular plates. Jeffrey pine has a huge beehive-shaped cone, five to fifteen inches long, which is very different from the less bulky cone of ponderosa pine which is generally under six inches in length. The scales of the Jeffrey pine cone are armed with recurved prickles at their tips. The lumber is cut with ponderosa pine and sold with it, since its quality and uses are almost identical.

DIGGER PINE, also called gray pine and bull pine, is another conifer discovered in California by David Douglas. The Indians living in this region where the pine grows were called "diggers" by the first settlers because they collected the edible seeds of the tree from the ground. Thus the pine became digger pine. This species is a thrifty tree, capable of surviving on the dry and inhospitable foothills of California's inland valleys. With its sparse, dusty green foliage, digger pine seems to have acquired some of the characteristics of the parched surroundings. It can live on as little as five inches of rainfall a year, and can endure temperatures of 110 degrees.

The crooked trunk of a digger pine forks into a few main limbs, in a fashion resembling an elm or oak more than a conifer. Trees are usually only a few feet in diameter and about fifty feet high. Digger pine, being a member of the pitch pine group, has three needles in a cluster. The drooping needles reach a length of twelve inches. Large chunky cones, six to ten inches long, bear scales tipped with sharp stout spines. The coarse-grained and brittle wood is of little commercial value, but the tree is useful in preventing soil erosion, forming an excellent ground cover in an otherwise practically treeless habitat.

The Sequoias

Most unique of all our native American trees, the two living species of Sequoia are found only on our Pacific Coast, in southern Oregon and California. In the long distant past, however, Sequoias were widely distributed over North America, Europe and Asia; fossil redwood cones have been found as far east as New Jersey. When the tree was first described, it was given the scientific name of "Sequoia" to honor Sequoyah, a Cherokee Indian chief of Georgia. The present-day Sequoias are in reality remnants of a once widespread race of trees. There are two living species, the coast redwood and the Sierra redwood (or Big Tree). Both are extremely long-lived because they were resistant to three of the worst enemies of trees: fungous diseases, insects and fire. The attacks of insects are discouraged by the high tannin content of the wood, which also gives it the reddish-brown color. The bark, often a foot thick, is an excellent protection against forest fires which may rage at the base of the trees. Many of the sequoias have great hollows burned out of the base, yet the trees have survived and seem little handicapped by their scars.

There are few experiences which can match that of following a dimly lit forest trail beneath these huge trees and feeling the immensity of living things which have stood their ground for so many centuries. It is awe-inspiring to think that those same branches which sway gently overhead have been doing this since before Columbus discovered America, before the destruction of the Roman Empire and even before the time of Christ. In these giant trees are combined graceful massiveness and airy charm with excessive strength and size.

COAST REDWOOD, sometimes referred to simply as redwood, is the taller and more graceful of the two sequoia species. Many individuals in the various redwood parks are over three hundred feet in height and sixty feet in circumference. They are shorter lived than the Sierra redwood, however; the oldest living coast redwoods are estimated to be only twenty-five hundred years

The Sequoias.

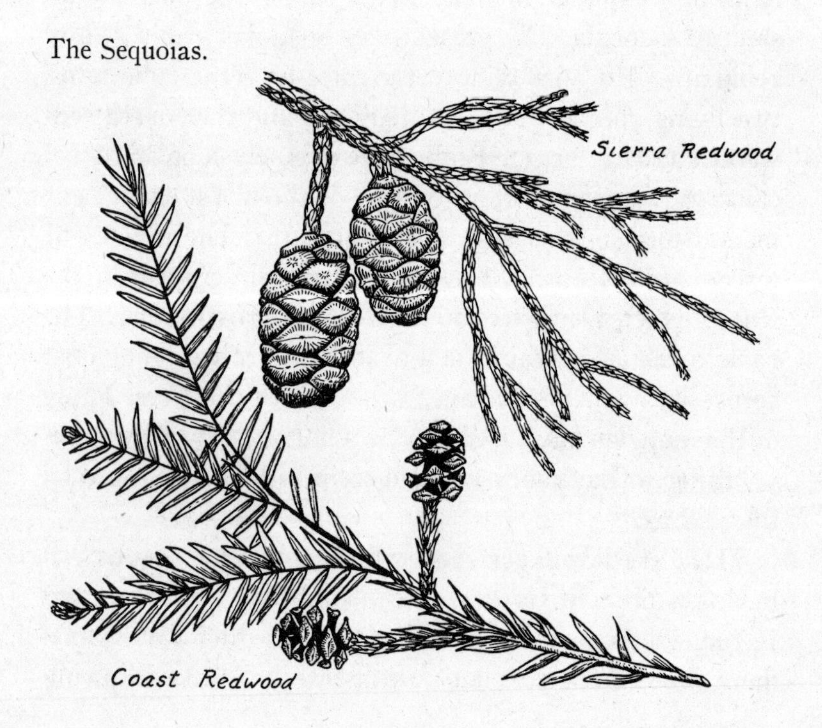

of age. Coast redwoods are trees of the California coast ranges, growing from sea level to 3,000 feet. They reach their best development in this region, which is bathed continuously by fog and drenched by rain.

The foliage, a bright yellowish-green, is similar to that of a yew or fir. The flat, sharply pointed needles are slightly less than an inch in length; they grow on either side of the branches, giving the redwood spray a flattened appearance. A graceful tapering trunk soars skyward like a column in a cathedral, often raising its straight shaft for a hundred feet before the first branch. On young trees the branches are short and drooping, forming a pyramid-shaped crown. The bark of old trees becomes ruddy gray or brown, and is fibrous and ridged lengthwise. The seed cones seem ridiculously small for such a huge tree, being rounded and only an inch in diameter. Few seeds germinate, but to offset this handicap coast redwood sprouts readily from the roots. In every redwood grove one can find thickets of vigorous young trees surrounding old stumps and remains of patriarchs long dead. Redwood lumber is of considerable commercial importance since it is easy to work and resists decay. It is best known for its use as shingles, exterior trim and siding for homes.

It is not surprising that this famous tree, combining scientific interest with usefulness and beauty, has been selected as the state tree of California.

SIERRA REDWOOD, or Big Tree, grows in a much more restricted area than the coast redwood. This species is found inland in about seventy groves, at altitudes of 4,000 to 8,000 feet, from Lake Tahoe to the southern tip of the Sierras. This species, more massive and stocky than the coast redwood, has a tremendous trunk with a very small crown of foliage. Many Sierra redwoods are ninety to one hundred feet in circumference, as compared to the sixty- or seventy-foot girth of the coast redwoods. But their height seldom exceeds two hundred fifty feet. Botanists are agreed that this species includes the oldest of living things. The largest trees whose age has been scientifically measured by trunk borings or ring counts are computed to be at least 4,000 years old. The General Sherman tree and President tree in Sequoia National Park, and the Grizzly Giant in Yosemite, are thought to be the three oldest trees on earth.

Sierra redwoods rarely grow in pure stands but are found towering over their neighbors, which include sugar pine, ponderosa pine, incense cedar and Douglas fir. The foliage is very different from that of the coast redwood, consisting of overlapping scale-like leaves which form bright green sprays resembling bald cypress or red cedar. The spongy and fibrous thick bark is a warm reddish-brown, with vertical ridges which contribute a fluted contour to the trunk. Seed cones develop in early spring, and mature into egg-shaped cones with thick scales, 2 to 3 inches in length. The seeds germinate readily, especially in the more sunny sites where the ground is free of needles. Sierra redwood does not form root sprouts, as the coast redwood does. Since the wood is brittle and of little commercial value, the greatest asset of this native American giant is its scientific uniqueness and its majestic beauty which yearly attract a multitude of visitors.

The Grizzly Giant is a veteran Sierra Redwood in the Mariposa Grove, Yosemite National Park; it is well over 3,000 years old.

Other Needle-leaved Conifers

The northern part of the Rocky Mountain forest is continuous with the Pacific Coast forest in Washington and Oregon. Thus it is not surprising to find in this area many of the evergreens which we have previously met in the Rockies. We have already mentioned this fact in describing the pines of the Pacific Coast. Grand fir, white fir and alpine fir are all found in the Pacific Northwest, as are Douglas fir, Engelmann spruce and western larch. Three of these—Douglas fir, white fir and grand fir—are also found in California. In addition, a few new species with needle-like leaves are likely to be encountered along our western trails. These are western hemlock and golden fir.

WESTERN HEMLOCK, or Pacific hemlock, is an overgrown edition of the eastern hemlock. Found in Washington and Oregon, and to a lesser extent in the northern Rockies, this conifer thrives in the humid coastal region. It reaches its greatest development on the west slopes of the Cascade Mountains at altitudes of 1,500 to 3,500 feet. It is rare in California except in a restricted area of the northern part of the state, near the seacoast. Western hemlock is a tall tree with a narrow pyramid-shaped crown, distinctive because of its lustrous green, feathery foliage and drooping branchlets. A tree in Olympic National Park of Washington has a circumference of 27 feet and is 125 feet high. Western hemlock is the state tree of Washington.

The flat narrow needles have the shape of an eastern hemlock's, but are three-quarters of an inch in length.

Western hemlock bark is reddish-brown and deeply furrowed, very rich in tannin. Small reddish-brown cones are produced, about an inch in length; they hang from the ends of the smaller branches in the same fashion that eastern hemlock cones do. The western species is an important timber tree, its wood being suitable for flooring, sheathing, framing and pulpwood.

GOLDEN FIR, also known as California red fir, Shasta fir and white fir, is the largest of our native firs. A specimen in Lassen Volcanic National Park is 25 feet in circumference and 168 feet high. This species is a tall symmetrical tree with a spire-like crown of blue-green foliage. It grows on high mountain slopes, at altitudes of 5,000 to 9,000 feet, being especially common on high mountain slopes of Mt. Shasta and in the Sierras. The lower branches tend to droop and cover the base of the tree, while the uppermost branches have an upward trend.

The four-angled needles of golden fir are blunt-tipped, slightly less than an inch in length, and curving inward so that they cover the upper sides of the branches. As is

Other Pacific Coast Conifers.

typical of all firs, the purplish-green cones stand erect on the branches; each cone is thick and cylindrical, four to eight inches in length. The cone scales drop off in the fall, so that the spike-like core stands alone on the branches during the winter. The soft, light and fine-grained wood is used for general building construction. Young trees have a chalky white bark, but that of old trees is purplish with deep zigzag furrows and narrow ridges. Resin blisters, like those on the balsam fir, are the source of Canada Balsam used in mounting microscope slides.

The Scale-leaved Evergreens

All of the conifers which we have met so far on our western trails have had foliage in the form of needles, either long and slender as in the pines, or shorter and flattened as in the firs, hemlocks and yew. Other evergreens have very small, scale-like, overlapping leaves, a fraction of an inch in length, and overlapping each other to cover the twigs completely. We have already seen this type of foliage in the Sierra redwood.

WESTERN RED CEDAR, or giant arbor vitae, is one of the largest trees on the Pacific Coast. A tree in Olympic National Park of Washington has a circumference of 62 feet. Many trees reach a height of one hundred fifty feet. It grows along the Pacific Coast from Washington to northern California, thriving on moist sites from sea level to 7,000 feet. From a distance this conifer can be recognized by its swollen base and massive tapering trunk, marked by fluted ridges.

The foliage consists, like that of the eastern arbor vitae,

of shiny dark green scale-leaves an eighth of an inch, or less, in length forming a noticeably flattened and lacy spray. The smaller branches, when crushed, are very pleasantly aromatic. Western red cedar bark is fibrous and reddish-brown, peeling readily into long tough strips. These were used by the Indians for weaving baskets and as ropes and fish lines. The small, leathery, brown cones, a half inch in length, consist of only six scales; empty cones remain upturned on the branches during the winter. Western red cedar's remarkable durability, when exposed to wind and weather, makes it the number one shingle material; it is also used for exterior finish and siding.

INCENSE CEDAR is a familiar evergreen throughout California where it grows singly or in groves in the same forest community with ponderosa and sugar pines. A tall and stately tree, it can be identified by its compact column-like crown of yellowish-green foliage and by its

Scale-leaved Evergreens of the West.

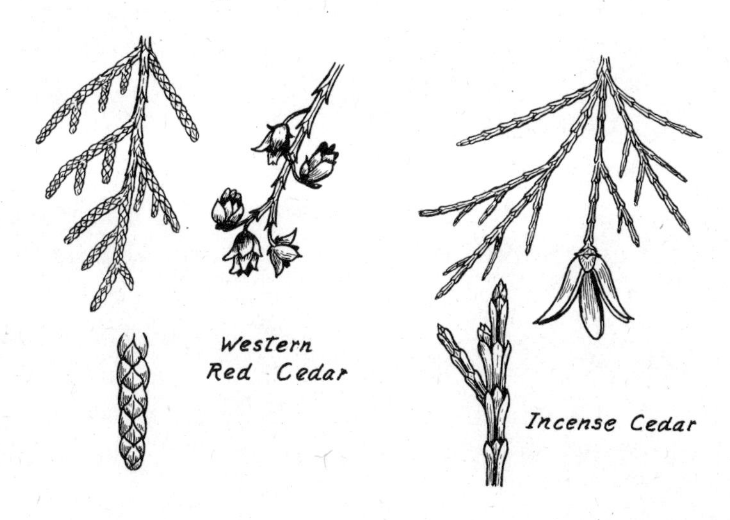

bright cinnamon-red trunk, whose shreddy bark is deeply furrowed into lengthwise ridges. A specimen in Yosemite National Park has a girth of 28 feet and is 143 feet high.

Incense cedar has small scale-like leaves with sharply pointed tip and long leaf base which sheaths the twig; like arbor vitae, the foliage, in flattened sprays, has a pungent and aromatic odor. When the male cones develop, in late winter, they discharge their pollen in such quantity that it often colors the snow with the golden powder. The slender urn-shaped seed cones, about an inch in length, consist of six scales arranged in pairs. Incense cedar wood is fragrant and attractive in color, suitable for cedar chests, cabinets, pencils, and Venetian blinds.

WESTERN JUNIPER, or Sierra juniper, is a stocky tree with a low broad crown; we encounter it where our trail leads over exposed hillsides and dry canyon slopes, chiefly in California at altitudes of 3,000 feet or more. A massive veteran in Stanislaus National Forest of California is 40 feet in circumference but only 80 feet high. This species can survive in extremely arid surroundings because of its huge and effective root system. Western juniper foliage, a pale ashy green, consists of two kinds of leaves, as is true of the eastern red cedar also. Young growth develops pointed, awl-shaped leaves which make the twigs prickly to touch. On older branches the leaves are scale-like, overlapping to form a stout rounded spray. Male flowers are produced on one tree, female flowers on another. Near the ends of the smaller branches are borne the typical juniper fruit, instead of a cone: a blue-black berry about a third of an inch in diameter and covered with a whitish bloom. The wood is of little commercial value, but the tree is a useful pioneer in colonizing unfavorable vegetation sites.

The Oaks

The lack in variety of deciduous trees in the Rocky Mountain forest was noticeable in comparison to the numerous broad-leaved species mingling with the conifers of the northern and southern forests. The woods of the Pacific Coast, on the other hand, are more like those in the eastern states in having a considerable number of evergreen and deciduous trees growing together. The largest group, as in the East, is the oaks. They can be recognized when in blossom by the drooping catkins of pollen-bearing flowers, and when in fruit by the familiar acorns. Two deciduous oaks of the Pacific Coast are California white oak and California black oak. Two evergreen oaks include the California live oak and canyon live oak.

CALIFORNIA WHITE OAK is also known as valley oak and valley white oak. A large tree with an elm-like habit when young, it develops a broad graceful crown with distinctive drooping branchlets. This oak thrives at low altitudes in the lowlands between the Sierras and the seacoast, reaching its best development in the hot moist valleys at altitudes below 4,000 feet. A specimen at Chico, 96 feet in height, has a circumference of 28 feet.

The leathery but deciduous leaves, about three inches in length, are divided into seven to eleven lobes, rounded like those of the eastern white oak. Dark green on the upper surface, the leaves are gray on the underside. The hairy covering of the leaves is a protection against the hot drying winds. The gray or brown bark is deeply furrowed, and broken into thick plates. California white oak acorns have chestnut-brown nuts, slender and pointed, averaging slightly less than two inches in length; their sweet kernel was eaten by the California Indians. Today the tree is useful only for shade and fuel.

CALIFORNIA BLACK OAK, resembling the eastern black oak, can be distinguished by the sharply pointed lobes of the leaves, a contrast to the rounded lobes of the two preceding species. This oak grows in northern California and southern Oregon, reaching circumferences of 25 feet and heights of 125 feet. The trunk is often leaning, and the large limbs form an irregular broad crown. California black oak often grows among ponderosa pines on mountain slopes and in canyons. The thick deciduous leaves are gracefully proportioned, four to ten inches long, and divided deeply by the indentations between the bristle-tipped lobes, of which there are seven. This oak can also be identified by the rounded acorns, an inch in length, set in deep scaly cups.

CALIFORNIA LIVE OAK is the familiar evergreen oak of southern California, where it is the western equivalent of the live oak found in the southern states. It is also called holly-leaved oak and coast live oak. A short massive trunk divides into spreading horizontal limbs, which lend twisted and crooked support to a wide-spreading low crown of foliage. This oak can tolerate dry and hot habitats where few other woody plants its size can survive. Southern California hillsides are dotted with the dark green domes of the low-growing live oaks. At Gilroy,

California, a record-sized tree measures 38 feet in circumference, although only 88 feet in height.

Live oaks are considered evergreen, since the tree is always covered with foliage. But actually the leaves remain on the branches only until the second spring, when the new crop of foliage has appeared. Each thick, stiff leaf is elliptical, an inch or two in length, and paler on the under side. The tip may be sharply pointed or rounded; the margins of some leaves are spiny toothed, like holly,

Oaks of the Pacific Coast.

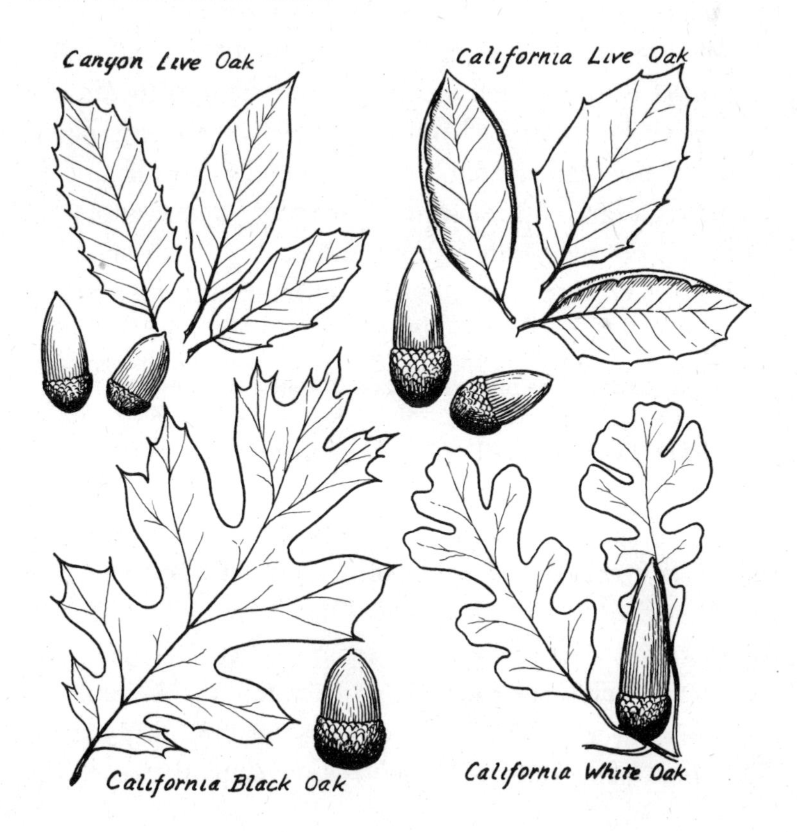

while others are smoother and inrolled. The unusual acorns are long and tapering, with a pointed tip; they are set in a deep cup.

CANYON LIVE OAK is a medium-sized evergreen oak of narrow mountain valleys and canyons, where it thrives in sandy and gravelly soil. Most trees are under 3 feet in diameter and 80 feet in height. The elliptical or oval leaves, an inch or two long, may be smooth edged or spiny toothed. They are always thick and leathery, bright yellowish-green on the upper side and whitish beneath. A short trunk divides near the ground into widely spreading branches, forming a round-topped crown. The gray or reddish-brown bark is covered with small flaking scales, in contrast to the dark brown bark of the California live oak which is furrowed into irregular plates and ridges. Canyon live oak is found throughout California and in nearby Oregon and Arizona. Broad egg-shaped nuts, an inch or two in length, are set in deep cups; these cylindrical nuts are the best recognition feature of the species.

Other Western Broad-leaved Trees

Many of the western broad-leaved trees are readily recognized by visitors because of their similarity to common eastern species. This is especially true of the western species of cottonwood, sycamore, dogwood, maple and ash.

BLACK COTTONWOOD, also known as California poplar and western balsam poplar, is one of the tallest western deciduous trees. It is common throughout the northern Rocky Mountain region as well as in the three Pacific Coast states. These trees frequently reach diameters of 3 and 4 feet, and heights of 125 feet; their favorite haunts are river bottoms, sand bars, and edges of streams. The gray smooth bark of young trees becomes furrowed and ridged in older trees. Broadly triangular leaves have a rounded base and pointed tips; they reach a length of six inches. Black cottonwood foliage is a dark shiny green on the upper surface, and whitish or rusty beneath.

CALIFORNIA SYCAMORE, or buttonball tree, is a medium-sized tree growing to a height of 70 or 80 feet. Like the eastern sycamore it grows best in the vicinity of water, and therefore is a common tree along canyon trails beside mountain streams. A familiar identification mark, as in the eastern sycamore, is the mottled bark, new white or yellow patches being exposed as the older darker bark sloughs off. The light yellowish green leaves, sometimes as large as ten or eleven inches in length, have three or five lobes, each with long tapering points. Another recognition tag is the ball-like cluster of seeds, which hangs in groups of four or five from the branches all winter.

PACIFIC DOGWOOD, or western dogwood, is a small tree of rich woods, shaded valleys and damp ravines; its range is from northern California to Washington. Like its eastern relative, it is easily identified when in blossom or fruit. Each cluster of tiny yellow flowers is surrounded by four or six conspicuous spreading bracts, usually white, although pink tints are sometimes found. The blossoms are larger than those of the eastern dogwood, reaching a diameter of five inches. The orange or red berries are about half an inch long. Pacific dogwood bark is reddish-brown and smooth. Its oval leaves, arranged in pairs along the branches, have smooth margins and conspicuous veins which curve to the tips, paralleling the edges of the leaf.

BIGLEAF MAPLE, or broadleaf maple, is a large tree found along the same trails as the Pacific dogwood; the only large maple of the Pacific Coast, it attains a circumference of 28 feet and a stature of 80 feet. Open grown trees have short trunks and a broad crown of shiny, dark green foliage; the gray bark is deeply furrowed, with scaly ridges. Bigleaf maple leaves, arranged in pairs like the eastern maples, are very large (as implied by the name), some reaching a length of twelve inches. The margins are deeply cut into three or five lobes, and may have additional smaller lobes. Fragrant clusters of yellow blossoms appear on the branches after the leaves develop; in late summer the "keys," which are the fruits, hang in small groups from the limbs. Each key is almost two inches in length, its basal seeds covered with bristly hairs.

OREGON ASH is the only ash which is of value as a timber tree on the Pacific Coast; it is found from Washington southward to California. The long clean straight trunk, like the eastern ashes, bears a narrow crown of foliage. It is frequent along trails which lead beside streams and along flood plains; here Oregon ash grows together with bigleaf maple and sycamore. The dark gray bark has the same diamond-shaped fissures and interlacing ridges which aid in identifying some of the eastern ashes. Large compound leaves occur in pairs, each leaf with five or seven elliptical leaflets, three to four inches in length. Inconspicuous male and female flowers develop on separate trees in clusters, as the leaves unfold. The wind-

The Washington Palm, a native of the Southern California desert region, develops a tall slender trunk, often sheathed in a thatch of dead leaves, hanging downwards below the crown.

dispersed fruits, shaped like the blade of an oar, hang in thick bunches from the female flowering tree.

MADRONA, or madrono tree, is a distinctive small tree found only along the Pacific Coast, from northern California to Washington. It prefers cool mountain canyons and valleys in the foothills. This tree is easily recognized by the bright red bark of the younger branches, satiny smooth and peeling; the dark green upper surface of the leaves is a contrast to the whiter under side. Small white flowers, like those of lily of the valley, are grouped in showy clusters; in autumn they produce orange-red berries, a half-inch in diameter. Madrona is one of the most colorful of the native broad-leaved trees of California.

Washington Palm

Southern California, like southern Florida, has a climate which encourages growth of subtropical species of trees. Florida has its native cabbage and royal palms; California has its Washington, or desert, palm.

WASHINGTON PALM was named in honor of George Washington. This palm grows naturally in a restricted portion of southern California, known as the Colorado Desert, and in a few mountain canyons bordering the desert. Best known are the groves of palms at Palm Canyon, Twenty-Nine Palms, and other nearby winter resorts. The palms have been transplanted over most of southern and central California, and have become the most common street tree in the Los Angeles area. Two palms planted by Jesuits on San Pedro Street in

Los Angeles are said to be two hundred years old; they are 3 feet in diameter and 90 feet high.

The cinnamon-brown slender trunk tapers very little for the forty or fifty feet of its stature; at the top is borne a spherical cluster of thirty or more huge fan-shaped leaves. Each leaf, circular in outline, and slashed almost to its base into numerous ribbon-like segments, grows at the end of a stiff leaf-stalk five feet in length. The two edges of the stalk are armed with sharp spines. As new leaves are produced each year, the old dead leaves remain attached but hang downward to form a brown thatch over the upper portion of the trunk. In time these fall off, revealing the armor of leaf-bases, already familiar in the Florida cabbage palm. Near the base of the trunk, these leaf-stalks also disappear, leaving the trunk smooth. Many small white flowers are borne in huge clusters at the base of the leaves; these become drooping clusters of black berry-like fruits in summer. Washington palms are untidy trees, but they lend a distinctly tropical aspect to many California streets and parks, and they thrive with very little water—a definite advantage in a semi-desert area where irrigation is expensive.

The Monkey Puzzle tree is a unique ornamental conifer grown in Florida and California.

Chapter 11

ROADSIDE TRAILS IN THE SOUTHWEST

THE SOUTHWESTERN STATES, and especially California, have a climate favorable to the introduction of a number of warm-climate trees, especially if they are capable of enduring drought conditions. Even though there is not an abundance of water, as there is in Florida, many of the subtropical ornamentals of the Southeast will succeed if artificially supplied with water. Thus a number of the trees which were described in Chapter Eight can be found in California and Arizona: Norfolk Island pine, Australian pine jacaranda, princess tree, banana tree, traveler's tree and various palms. In addition we find new immigrants, many of them from Australia and the west coast of South America which seem particularly suited to the climate of the Southwest.

The Introduced Conifers

MONKEY PUZZLE is an evergreen with strange appearance, closely related to the Norfolk Island pine. In its native home on the western slopes of the Andes in Chile it reaches heights of a hundred feet; under cultivation in this country it is usually a lawn tree, rarely more than twenty-five feet in height. It has the regular pyramid-shaped outline of the familiar conifers, but the symmetrical whorls of branches produce rope-like smaller branches which form an intricate jungle of limbs, thus explaining the unusual name. The dark green foliage consists of stiff awl-shaped leaves an inch or two in length, and sharply pointed; they arise in closely-overlapping series which acts as a spiny armor for the branch. Monkey puzzle is distinctly a botanical oddity, grown more for its unusual shape and foliage than for its use as a shade or street tree.

DEODAR CEDAR, another common ornamental evergreen of the conifer group, is prized for its graceful drooping foliage. In its general appearance it resembles a larch more than a cedar. A native of the Himalayan region, its relative, the cedar of Lebanon, is frequently mentioned in the Bible. In its home range it becomes a massive tree, a hundred feet in height; cultivated specimens in this country are much smaller and less ponderous in appearance. The dark bluish-green foliage consists of three-angled needles in bunches, each needle being an inch or two in length. Conspicuous reddish-brown cones grow upright on the branches, like those of the firs.

The Broad-leaved Immigrants

CAMPHOR TREE has been introduced into the Southwest from its native home in tropical Asia and China. It is one of the few ornamental trees of the West Coast with simple leaves; each elliptical leaf, several inches in length, tapers to a point. Old leaves are shiny green on the upper surface but grayish-white on the underside. The small, yellow flowers are grouped in clusters two or three inches in length; they develop into black berries less than an inch in diameter. Medicinal camphor is obtained from the wood and leaves of trees in their native home;

Introduced Trees of the Pacific Coast.

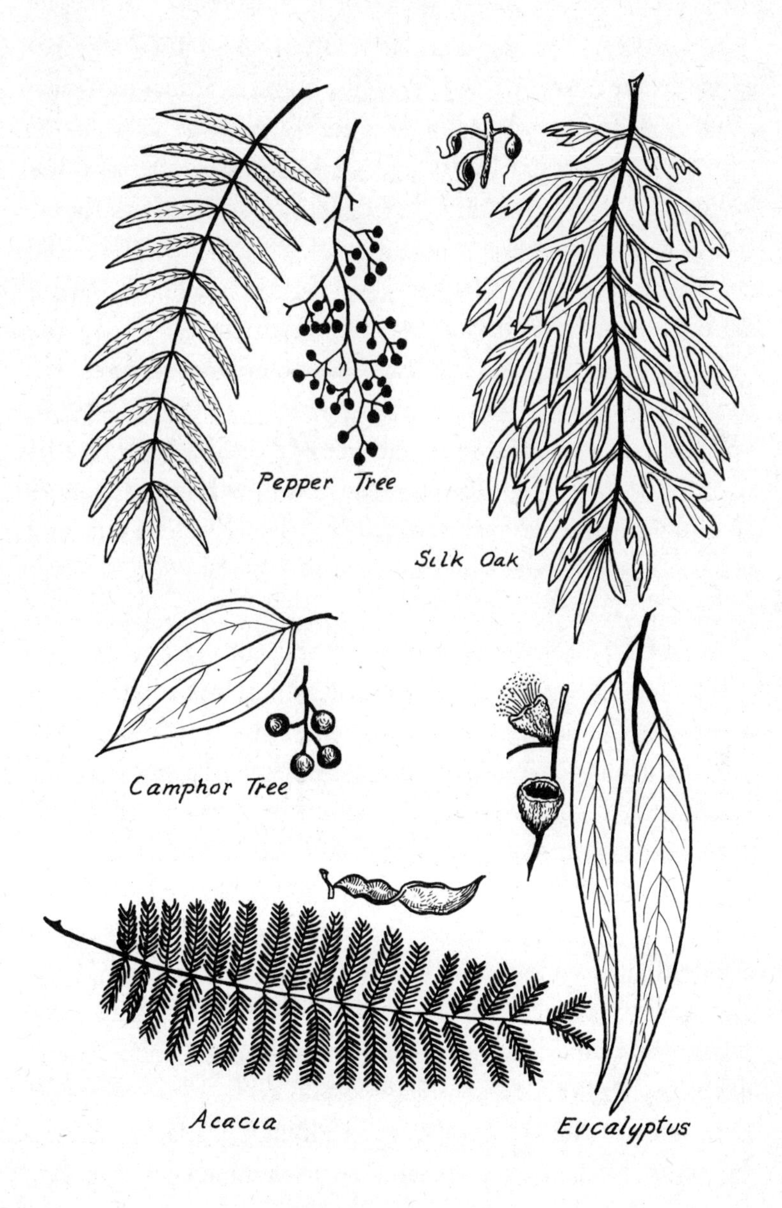

the camphor odor can be identified when the foliage of the ornamental tree is crushed.

SILK OAK is also known as Australian fern tree because of the feathery and fern-like foliage; it is a medium-sized tree from Australia frequently planted as a street tree in California. In its native home silk oak reaches heights of a hundred and fifty feet. In spite of its name, this is not an oak, but a member of a family of trees and shrubs native to Australia and South America. Being drought resistant, it does well without irrigation in the drier portions of the state. The large compound leaves, six to ten inches long, bear leaflets which are sharply lobed and toothed; the silky white nature of the under surface of the leaflets is responsible for the common name. Clusters of small orange or yellow flowers arise on the trunk and main branches. Silk oak has a curved black pod less than an inch in length.

ACACIA, or silver wattle, is an unforgettable tree when seen in spring at the height of its flowering. Street after street in many California cities have a golden yellow aura as every acacia tree is covered with dainty balls of small bright-yellow blossoms. The tiny flowers, of which the conspicuous part is the stamens, are grouped in compact spherical clusters, about half an inch in diameter or less. Acacia, a member of the pea family imported from Australia, is widely used as a street tree throughout the Southwest. The foliage is feathery and gray-green, consisting of twice compound leaves three to six inches long, with tiny leaflets. Acacia fruits, as is to be expected from a member of the pea family, are reddish pods, a few inches in length. Some acacia species are unusual in that they lack

Acacia blossoms are clustered in compact golden-yellow balls.

leaves and instead develop leaf-like flattened green stems.

PEPPER TREE has become so well established in California and Arizona that naturalized trees can sometimes be found on the outskirts of towns. Being drought resistant like the silk oak, pepper trees thrive in many California towns where water is scarce. They were introduced into this country from Peru; their closest American relative is sumac. The low spreading crown and drooping branches are like those of the weeping willow; the weeping effect is heightened by the compound leaves, sometimes a foot in length, which also hang downwards. Each leaf bears about twenty pairs of narrow pointed leaflets, each an inch or two in length. The small yellowish-white flowers are either male or female, and the sexes occur on separate trees. Female flowers form drooping clusters of small berries which resemble red beads; remaining on the tree all winter, they add a decorative touch to a tree which is already ornamental because of its foliage.

EUCALYPTUS includes a number of species of an Australian tree, variously known as Australian gum, blue gum or red gum. They have become as common in California as elms in New England, and are today accepted as a natural part of the landscape. In its native home Eucalyptus grow to be huge trees, almost equalling the Sequoias in stature. They grow rapidly and serve a variety of purposes; arch over streets, act as a windbreak for citrus groves, and form wooded areas in parks and on campuses. Many individuals grow tall and straight, with a narrow open crown of foliage. The common blue gum has an aromatic brown bark which peels off in long strips to reveal the smooth gray bark underneath. At a distance the light mottled bark might be mistaken for that of a sycamore. Occasionally long strips of bark hang down from the branches and collect on the ground beneath the trees. Eucalyptus leaves are simple, with smooth margins and a slender tapering shape; some species have sickle-shaped leaves with pointed tips. Eucalyptus flowers are white, yellow or scarlet, depending upon the species. They occur in spherical clusters and are unusual in that the sepals and petals have fused to form a rather hard lid over the other floral parts. This lid falls off at maturity, exposing the stamens, which are the conspicuous part of the flower. Flower cup and lid are aromatic and covered with

Eucalyptus has adapted itself well to the California climate; here a vista of the San Bernadino range can be seen through a young grove of these Australian trees.

a blue-gray waxy bloom. From the tree comes eucalyptol, an ingredient in many medicinal preparations.

The Introduced Palms

DATE PALM, originally introduced into the United States for its fruit, has become an ornamental tree in many parts of the Southwest. Its ancestral home is considered to have been somewhere near Persia; like the coconut palm, it is today unknown in the wild state. Date palms were growing in the irrigated deserts of Arabia over five thousand years ago. These palms, unlike the royal and coconut palms, are majestic trees eighty feet or more in height, with stout trunks and a crown of large gracefully-arching leaves. The trunks are roughened by old persisting leaf bases. Each huge leaf consists of many ribbon-like leaflets folded lengthwise and arranged feather-like along the midrib. Clusters of a thousand or more small yellow blossoms grow out of leathery sheaths; they develop into yellowish-red fruits which turn purple or black as they become ripe dates.

CANARY ISLAND PALM is a popular palm for ornamental use in southern California. It closely resembles the date palm, with which it can be easily confused. Canary Island palm, however, is more slender in all its proportions and the foliage crown usually contains many more leaves. As its name indicates, it has been introduced from the Canary Islands. Growth of this palm under cultivation is very rapid. A tree ten years old developed a trunk four feet high, three feet in diameter, with a crown of over a hundred leaves with a twenty-five foot spread!

Date Palms have massive trunks and huge arching crowns of graceful compound leaves.

PLUME PALM is a relative of the coconut palm, which it resembles in many ways; it is extensively planted as a street tree in the Los Angeles area. This palm has been introduced from Brazil. The slender graceful trunk, marked at intervals by rings, is topped by a small cluster of gracefully arching compound leaves. Each leaf, which may reach a length of fifteen feet, bears many small ribbon-like leaflets. Young plume palms are entitled to the name, for their general appearance is that of a dainty plume of foliage atop a slender support.

In the preceding pages we have endeavored to present a picture, on a broad scale, of the general features of our American forests and of the individual traits of the most common tree citizens which inhabit them. In addition to meeting our "native sons" among the trees, you have also become acquainted with some of the immigrant species from foreign lands. Together they make an impressive array of trees with a wide variety of personalities and uses, living in a diversified range of habitats.

Some of us may now feel better acquainted with the trees of the forest community at our back door. Others may be eager to meet the members of new forest regions in the north, east, south, and west when the opportunity to travel presents itself. Others—the lucky naturalists—may even now be planning a visit to the seacoast of Acadia National Park, to the great swamps of the Everglades, to Yosemite National Park, to Palm Canyon, or to the Redwood Highway. In these, and a dozen other places where unusual American trees grow, we hope that your appreciation of the forest community will have been increased by the information presented in this book.

But to all our readers, may your friendship with trees grow greater and deeper as the years go by. There are few rewards to equal those of feeling at home among our tree neighbors, especially when we can think of trees as species and individuals, rather than as impersonal stands of timber and so many miles of wilderness to be pierced by a dual-line highway.

C. J. H.

INDEX

Each kind of tree has a scientific name as well as a common one; the advantage of the scientific name is that there is only one for each kind of tree. Many trees have several common names, as we have discovered in the previous chapters. Scientific names must therefore be used if we wish to be accurate. When you refer to a tree by its scientific name you do not leave any room for doubt as to what kind of tree you are describing.

The naming of trees is a very methodical matter. Each kind of tree has a double name, just as each person has a first and last name. We refer to William Smith, putting the family name last and the individual name first. But in scientific names, the reverse is true. Sweet birch is *Betula lenta,* the *"Betula"* meaning the birch group and the *"lenta"* the particular kind of birch known as sweet birch. In other words it is like saying "Smith, William." Each individual kind of tree is a species, so that all sweet birches are known as *"Betula lenta."* Another kind of birch, such as river birch, is *Betula nigra,* the *"nigra"* referring to the other species which we call river birch, but the group name remains the same. *"Betula,"* the group name, refers to the genus, which technically means a group of related species.

Scientists who make a study of classifying plants and animals have worked out a system whereby related genera (the plural of genus) are considered to be part of a larger unit, the family. This is much like having three different Smith groups, all descended from a common grandfather and therefore having many traits in common. When we list trees by species, genera and families we make it easier to remember special features of the trees because those with similar traits are grouped together. This is much more satisfactory than an alphabetical arrangement of trees by their common names, which gives no indication of what each tree may be like.

All our trees are grouped into two large categories. One includes all those trees which reproduce by cones and unprotected seeds; that is, the seed is not surrounded by a fruit. Most of the trees in this category are evergreen, and possess needle-like or scale-like leaves. They are known as GYMNOSPERMS. The other category includes all those trees which reproduce by some kind of flower (which includes catkins) and by seeds embedded in fruits. Most of the trees in this category are deciduous with broad thin leaves. They are known as ANGIOSPERMS.

THE GYMNOSPERM TREES

	Common Name	Scientific Name	*Page*
ARAUCARIA FAMILY	Norfolk Island pine	*Araucaria excelsa*	167
	Monkey puzzle tree	*Araucaria araucana*	221
CYPRESS FAMILY	Arizona cypress	*Cupressus glabra*	192
	Arbor vitae	*Thuja occidentalis*	66
	Incense cedar	*Libocedrus decurrens*	209
	Red cedar	*Juniperus virginiana*	68
	Western juniper	*Juniperus occidentalis*	210
	Utah juniper	*Juniperus osteosperma*	192
	Western red cedar	*Thuja plicata*	208
MAIDENHAIR FAMILY	Maidenhair tree	*Ginkgo biloba*	130
PINE FAMILY	Austrian pine	*Pinus nigra*	126
	Jack pine	*Pinus banksiana*	57
	Pitch pine	*Pinus rigida*	58
(Eastern Pines)	Red pine	*Pinus resinosa*	57
	Scotch pine	*Pinus sylvestris*	128
	White pine	*Pinus strobus*	56

THE GYMNOSPERM TREES (*Continued*)

	Common Name	Scientific Name	*Page*
	Loblolly pine	*Pinus taeda*	141
	Longleaf pine	*Pinus palustris*	140
(Southern Pines)	Shortleaf pine	*Pinus echinata*	143
	Slash pine	*Pinus caribaea*	142
	Virginia pine	*Pinus virginiana*	144
	Digger pine	*Pinus sabiniana*	200
	Jeffrey pine	*Pinus jeffreyi*	199
	Lodgepole pine	*Pinus contorta*	182
(Western Pines)	Pinyon	*Pinus edulis*	182
	Ponderosa pine	*Pinus ponderosa*	181
	Sugar pine	*Pinus lambertiana*	198
	Western white pine	*Pinus monticola*	179
	Colorado blue spruce	*Picea pungens*	189
	Engelmann spruce	*Picea engelmanni*	188
(Spruces)	Norway spruce	*Picea excelsa*	128
	Red spruce	*Picea rubens*	60
	White spruce	*Picea glauca*	61
	Douglas fir	*Pseudotsuga douglasi*	186
	Alpine fir	*Abies lasiocarpa*	186
	Balsam fir	*Abies balsamea*	62
(Firs)	Grand fir	*Abies grandis*	182
	White fir	*Abies concolor*	183
	Eastern hemlock	*Tsuga canadensis*	64
(Hemlocks)	Western hemlock	*Tsuga heterophylla*	206
	Eastern larch	*Larix laricina*	65
	Western larch	*Larix occidentalis*	190
	Deodar cedar	*Cedrus deodara*	222
REDWOOD FAMILY	Coast redwood	*Sequoia sempervirens*	202
	Sierra redwood	*Sequoia gigantea*	203
	Bald cypress	*Taxodium distichum*	145

THE ANGIOSPERM TREES

	Common Name	Scientific Name	Page
AILANTHUS FAMILY	Tree of Heaven	*Ailanthus altissima*	133
ASH FAMILY	Black ash	*Fraxinus nigra*	123
	Oregon ash	*Fraxinus oregona*	216
	White ash	*Fraxinus americana*	124
BANANA FAMILY	Banana tree	*Musa sapientum*	174
	Traveler's tree	*Ravenala madagascariensis*	176

THE ANGIOSPERM TREES (*Continued*)

	Common Name	Scientific Name	*Page*
BEECH FAMILY	American beech	*Fagus grandifolia*	99
	Chestnut	*Castanea dentata*	100
(Eastern Oaks)	Black oak	*Quercus velutina*	98
	Bur oak	*Quercus macrocarpa*	94
	Chestnut oak	*Quercus montana*	94
	Pin oak	*Quercus palustris*	96
	Post oak	*Quercus stellata*	92
	Red oak	*Quercus borealis*	95
	Scarlet oak	*Quercus coccinea*	97
	White oak	*Quercus alba*	91
(Southern Oaks)	Eastern live oak	*Quercus virginiana*	151
	Laurel oak	*Quercus laurifolia*	150
	Red oak	*Quercus falcata*	148
	Willow oak	*Quercus phellos*	150
(Western Oaks)	California live oak	*Quercus agrifolia*	212
	California white oak	*Quercus lobata*	211
	California black oak	*Quercus kelloggii*	212
	Canyon live oak	*Quercus chrysolepis*	214
BIRCH FAMILY	Gray birch	*Betula populifolia*	75
	Paper birch	*Betula papyrifera*	74
	River birch	*Betula nigra*	78
	Sweet birch	*Betula lenta*	77
	Yellow birch	*Betula lutea*	76
BIGNONIA FAMILY	Western catalpa	*Catalpa speciosa*	120
BLACK GUM FAMILY	Black gum	*Nyssa sylvatica*	106
CASUARINA FAMILY	Australian pine	*Casuarina equisetifolia*	168
DOGWOOD FAMILY	Eastern dogwood	*Cornus florida*	119
	Pacific dogwood	*Cornus nuttalli*	215
ELM FAMILY	American elm	*Ulmus americana*	84
	Hackberry	*Celtis occidentalis*	101
FIGWORT FAMILY	Princess tree	*Paulownia tomentosa*	169
HEATH FAMILY	Madrona	*Arbutus menziesii*	218
HORSE CHESTNUT FAMILY	Buckeye	*Aesculus glabra*	123
	Horse chestnut	*Aesculus hippocastanum*	132
HOLLY FAMILY	American holly	*Ilex opaca*	155
LAUREL FAMILY	Camphor tree	*Cinnamomum camphora*	222
	Sassafras	*Sassafras officinalis*	105

THE ANGIOSPERM TREES (*Continued*)

	Common Name	Scientific Name	*Page*
LINDEN FAMILY	Basswood	*Tilia glabra*	106
MANGROVE FAMILY	Red mangrove	*Rhizophora mangle*	160
MAGNOLIA FAMILY	Southern magnolia	*Magnolia grandiflora*	158
	Sweet bay	*Magnolia virginiana*	159
	Tulip tree	*Liriodendron tulipifera*	107
MYRTLE FAMILY	Blue gum	*Eucalyptus globulus*	226
MAHOGANY FAMILY	Chinaberry tree	*Melia species*	170
MAPLE FAMILY	Bigleaf maple	*Acer macrophyllum*	216
	Norway maple	*Acer platanoides*	132
	Red maple	*Acer rubrum*	80
	Silver maple	*Acer saccharinum*	81
	Sugar maple	*Acer saccharum*	79
MULBERRY FAMILY	Osage orange	*Maclura pomifera*	103
	Red mulberry	*Morus rubra*	101
	Strangling fig	*Ficus aurea*	160
PALM FAMILY	Cabbage palm	*Sabal palmetto*	163
	Coconut palm	*Cocos nucifera*	172
	Canary Island palm	*Phoenix canariensis*	228
	Date palm	*Phoenix dactylifera*	228
	Plume palm	*Cocos plumosa*	230
	Royal palm	*Roystonea regia*	164
	Washington palm	*Washingtonia filifera*	218
PEA FAMILY	Acacia	*Acacia decurrens*	224
	Black locust	*Robinia pseudoacacia*	118
	Honey locust	*Gleditsia triacanthus*	116
	Mimosa	*Albizia julibrissin*	171
	Royal poinciana	*Delonix regia*	172
	Redbud	*Cercis canadensis*	154
PROTEA FAMILY	Silk oak	*Grevillea robusta*	224
ROSE FAMILY	Black cherry	*Prunus serotina*	103
	Hawthorns	*Crataegus species*	104
	Mountain ash	*Sorbus americana*	82
SUMAC FAMILY	Pepper tree	*Schinus molle*	225
SYCAMORE FAMILY	Eastern sycamore	*Platanus occidentalis*	84
	California sycamore	*Platanus racemosa*	215
WALNUT FAMILY	Bitternut	*Carya cordiformis*	112
	Black walnut	*Juglans nigra*	109
	Butternut	*Juglans cinerea*	110
	Mockernut	*Carya tomentosa*	114
	Pecan	*Carya pecan*	112

THE ANGIOSPERM TREES (*Continued*)

	Common Name	Scientific Name	*Page*
	Pignut hickory	*Carya glabra*	114
	Shagbark hickory	*Carya ovata*	113
WILLOW FAMILY	Eastern cottonwood	*Populus deltoides*	72
	Black cottonwood	*Populus trichocarpa*	214
	Large tooth aspen	*Populus grandidentata*	72
	Lombardy poplar	*Populus nigra*	134
	Quaking aspen	*Populus tremuloides*	69
	Black willow	*Salix nigra*	86
	Weeping willow	*Salix babylonica*	135
WITCH HAZEL FAMILY	Sweet gum	*Liquidambar styraciflua*	152